Eat Up Slim Down!

2013 ANNUAL RECIPES

200 Simply Delicious Recipes for Permanent Weight Loss

From the editors
of
Prevention®

RODALE®

In all Rodale cookbooks, our mission is to provide delicious and nutritious recipes. Our recipes also meet the standards of the Rodale Test Kitchen for dependability, ease, practicality, and, most of all, great taste. To give us your comments, call (800) 848-4735.

Printed in the United States of America
Rodale Inc. makes every effort to use acid-free ⊗, recycled paper ♺.

Design by Elizabeth Neal
Photo credits can be found on page 347.

ISBN 978–1–60961–925–1

2 4 6 8 10 9 7 5 3 1 hardcover

We inspire and enable people to improve their lives and the world around them.
For more of our products visit prevention.com or call 800-848-4735.

Special Thanks

We would like to thank all the readers of *Prevention* magazine and prevention.com for sharing clever tips, delicious recipes, and their inspiring stories of weight loss success.

And sincere, heartfelt thanks to the four weight loss winners who shared their stories with us in personal profiles: Lynn Greenhalge, Catherine Zanoni, Aldith Diaz, and Shannon Hammer.

Contents

Introduction

ARE YOU READY TO BEGIN your weight loss journey? If so, you've come to the right place. This year's edition of *Eat Up Slim Down! is* packed with dozens of fresh ideas to help you reach your goals and more than 200 recipes to get you on your way to a slimmer new you.

However, there are a few things worth pointing out before we begin: If you've read more than a few diet books before, you might be tempted to skip over the first few chapters in this book and jump right into the recipes. That's perfectly understandable—after all, we have more than 75 full-color photos that are bound to whet your appetite. But by moving straight to the recipes, you would be missing out on some new insights about weight loss that will surprise you.

For example, should you even keep the word *diet* in your vocabulary? Some nutrition experts are starting to think that some of us might be better off without it. That's because they believe the road to health, and potentially long-term weight loss, is not about reaching a specific destination—a particular number on the scale. Rather, they advocate listening to your body and making small, incremental lifestyle changes that could have a dramatic impact on your well-being.

What kind of lifestyle changes are we talking about? Small changes, like making sure you're getting the best sleep possible (turn to page 13 to discover three ways to improve your sleep tonight), boosting your everyday activity level (start on page 10 to find 100 no-sweat ideas that could work for you), and learning how to load up your plate with the best foods—and in the right amounts (visit Chapter 4 for fruit and veggie tips and a handy portion control guide).

What you won't find in this collection is one-size-fits-all advice. That's because your weight loss journey is as unique as you are. What works for one person may not work for another. Just look at the stories of the four people we have profiled. Some counted every calorie while others found that they enjoyed being more active. Several found that once they finally gave themselves permission to eat what they liked, they tended to choose healthier options and lost weight in the long run. What's important is choosing what works best for you.

So what are you waiting for? Let's get started!

The Way to a New You

SOME WEIGHT LOSS PLANS would have you believe that the key to losing weight and keeping it off is simply to have a healthier relationship with food or avoiding a particular nutrient. And let's not forget the folks who point to exercise as the magic bullet for what ails you. But if it were really that easy, why then are so many of us still overweight?

The issue is that these approaches tend to oversimplify, and what works for one person may not work for another. That's why this book aims to help you take a personal approach to your weight loss journey.

Here you will find plenty of new ideas—as well as delicious recipes—to put to work for you. But before we get to all of that, let's start off with a rather groundbreaking question: Should you even be dieting at all?

THE END OF DIETING?

Here's a fact that may surprise you: The majority of Americans are serious about losing weight. In fact, at any given time, 53 percent of Americans are trying to slim down. But if this is true, why do so many people in this country remain overweight? The reality is that 8 out of 10 dieters regain their lost weight within 2 years, and nearly two-thirds pile on even more pounds.

Many experts believe this is because diets simply don't work for long-term weight loss. "If we had a 95 percent failure rate with a medication, it would never get approved by the FDA. Yet that's dieting's record," says Michelle May, MD, founder of Am I Hungry? Mindful Eating Workshops.

After decades of yo-yo dieting that only leaves them heavier than they were when they began, many women lose the will to work out and watch what they eat, and they begin dodging doctors who seem to blame all their problems on their weight. Some ultimately give up on dealing with health issues such as high blood pressure or elevated cholesterol, believing that without dramatic weight loss, any efforts are useless.

But according to a controversial new movement, it is possible to break this cycle of failed diets and poor health, even if you never end up in a pair of skinny jeans or in the safety zone of the Body Mass Index (BMI) chart.

It's known as Health at Every Size (HAES), and its principles are so radically simple that they can be difficult to grasp after a lifetime of trying to follow complicated plans full of rules, stages, calories, grams of fat, points, scales, and math.

HOW THE HEALTH AT EVERY SIZE (HAES) PROGRAM WORKS

The basic premise of this revolutionary new approach is that healthy behaviors can improve your life regardless of whether they result in a lower number on the scale. You abandon diets in favor of "intuitive eating," which means paying close attention to what you crave and how the foods you eat make you feel, as well as gradually learning to distinguish emotional hunger from the physical kind. For exercise, you identify any activity that provides enough fun that you don't need to force yourself to do it regularly. HAES also encourages you to love and respect your body just as it is—whatever size it is right now. At its core, HAES is about stripping away rigid ideas about food and fitness.

Though most women understand that dieting can be destructive, many who have found themselves in a yo-yo pattern find it's a hard cycle to break. At Green Mountain at Fox Run, a weight loss center in Vermont that specializes in helping women adopt the HAES approach, the staff keeps the scale under lock and key to remove the temptation for those who find the habits of fixating on the scale and calculating calories hard to break. Some clients have histories of eating disorders, and many have trouble learning to respond to real hunger cues as a signal to eat, which is among the most important skills they need to develop for the HAES approach to produce results.

"Intuitive eating tunes you in to your body so you know when you're really hungry and when you've had enough," says Marsha J.

Hudnall, RD, the program director at Green Mountain. And it's not all candy, ice cream, cheese, chips, and fries. "Some do end up eating more of those foods initially," Hudnall says. "But as you truly give yourself permission to eat what you want, you naturally gravitate to healthier choices."

In Green Mountain's program, women learn to eat more whole foods by discovering how satisfying and delicious these foods can be. Its kitchen turns out meals like walnut pesto-encrusted Vermont-raised chicken with roasted butternut squash and arugula salad, lemon-soy grilled flank steak with garlicky mashed potatoes and lemony asparagus, and bean-and-veggie wraps with chipotle-cucumber salad and carrot bisque.

There are cooking classes to teach women the skills they need to make food like this when they return home. Other classes help women uncover the emotional basis for many food cravings. Part of intuitive eating is realizing that sometimes you're hungry for things besides food, and there are ways other than eating to satisfy those needs.

CAN YOU BE HEALTHY AT ANY SIZE?

For most doctors, it's still hard to believe health improvements are possible without weight loss. "The research is very compelling that as your weight increases, your risk for several diseases increases also," says Wahida Karmally, DrPH, RD, director of nutrition at the Irving Institute for Clinical and Translational Research at Columbia University Medical Center.

Yet a growing body of evidence suggests the logic of the HAES movement may be right on track. One study sponsored by the National Institutes of Health randomly assigned 78 women to either an HAES program or a conventional diet program. The HAES women were coached in adopting healthy food, activity, and lifestyle choices but were given no rigid rules or restrictions. They also participated in support groups in which they dealt with issues regarding body acceptance and feelings that tied self-worth to their sizes. The women in the HAES program saw improvements (based on measures of blood pressure, cholesterol levels, activity levels, and depression) both at 6 months and at 2 years. The women in the dieting group lost weight and had improvements initially, but ultimately they went back to their old behaviors, weight, and blood measures within 2 years.

Some experts believe that the negative effects of yo-yo dieting go beyond the physical and emotional tolls of being overweight or obese. According to Linda Bacon, PhD, associate nutritionist at the University of California, Davis; nutrition professor at City College of San Francisco; and author of *Health at Every Size* (the bible of the HAES movement), many studies suggest that yo-yo dieting itself increases the risk of high blood pressure, insulin resistance, and high blood cholesterol. Studies also show that a vast majority of dieting ends up being yo-yo dieting: Up to two-thirds of people who lose weight regain it within 1 year, and nearly all the rest regain it within 5 years.

Many doctors fear that though HAES has helped numerous women make important health improvements and lifestyle changes, some participants will take the movement's

love-yourself-as-you-are mentality to mean it's okay to eat a half gallon of ice cream in one sitting or limit workouts to lifting the TV remote.

"We can't allow the effort to improve people's self-image to interfere with efforts to combat a serious medical concern," says David L. Katz, MD, MPH, director of Yale University's Prevention Research Center and an advisory board member at *Prevention* magazine. "I agree that not everybody can be an underwear model. But when 65 percent of American adults are overweight or obese, a landslide majority is failing."

However, a growing number of professionals believe that a paradigm shift is overdue. Deb Burgard, PhD, a psychologist based in the San Francisco Bay area who specializes in eating disorders, agrees that it's time to stop the single-minded focus on diets. "Studies show that even losing a little weight helps, but I think it's the things you do that help—the physical activity and nutrition intervention, not the weight loss itself," she says.

Even the detractors concede that if the message is articulated clearly and followed in good faith, HAES has its place for those who are determined to hop off the diet treadmill. "If we can talk people into pursuing health, especially people who have given up on it, HAES can do a lot more good than harm," says Dr. Katz. "Besides, most people who truly focus on eating well and exercising will find that the weight eventually takes care of itself."

CARVING YOUR OWN PATH: HOW TO FIND WHAT WORKS FOR YOU

Just as each of us seems to gain weight in our very own way, we take control of our health with approaches that are uniquely ours as well. The CDC performed a major study of people who lost weight and, more importantly, kept it off. The takeaway was clear: No single strategy worked for everyone. Some people ate less overall, while others cut out specific high-calorie treats such as presweetened beverages or fried foods. Others filled up on low-cal foods like fruits and vegetables. Once you find methods that work for you, it will become infinitely easier to stick with them for the rest of your life if you also incorporate the following four strategies:

Personalize your plan: Sit down now and begin by looking at the vulnerable parts of your day: the doughnut shop you pass on your way to work; the afternoon lull when you need a pick-me-up; the weekend downtime that draws you irresistibly to the TV, bowl of ice cream in hand. Think about what healthier options may be available to you in each situation so that if you do find yourself in that doughnut shop one morning, you are prepared to rely on a better alternative—the ham, egg, and cheese on an English muffin, for example.

Get moving: Like it or not, the research on this one is clear. Being more active is essential to long-term weight loss. However, the good news is you don't have to become an elite athlete to put this strategy to work for you. In fact, finding just a few key ways to boost your overall activity level can have a profound effect. In the next chapter, we've compiled a list of 100 different ways you might do just that—without even breaking a sweat!

Track your progress: Reaching your weight loss goal doesn't happen overnight, so one way you can keep your motivation level up is to keep a record of your incremental success. Think about how you might want to measure your progress without relying on your scale: Keep a journal to record your emotional journey and how your thoughts and feelings about food change over time; use your cell phone to snap a quick picture of yourself every week to see the slimmer you emerge; let your clothes be your guide to tell if you are fitting into them better. Whichever methods you prefer, think of a way at the outset to help you reflect on your unique path to health.

Get cooking: Here's the best way to know exactly what you are eating every day. Restaurants and delis are notorious for slipping extra calories into their dishes. So why not make a point of making it yourself? This book provides more than 200 delicious dishes that fit two main qualifications: They are simple to prepare and guaranteed to whet your appetite.

A No-Sweat Weight Loss Plan

AS WE DISCUSSED IN Chapter 1, losing weight—and keeping it off—requires a personal plan of action. But that last word, *action*, is key because we cannot overlook the amount of movement we incorporate into our lives and the impact it has on our waistlines.

Of course, many of us probably wish that were not the case. So often we're conditioned to think that our food choices have the biggest impact on our weight. But the truth is that desk jobs, long commutes, too much TV time—all that inactivity our daily routines dictate—can ultimately be about as fattening as a steady diet of bacon and bread. And despite what you may think, slipping on your sneakers for daily sweat sessions alone probably isn't enough to combat the slow slide toward sickness.

According to a study published in the *American Journal of Epidemiology*, women who sat for more than 6 hours each day had a 37 percent increased risk of premature death, compared with women who sat for less than 3, regardless of how often they hopped on a treadmill.

What's more, nearly all of us are at risk. The average American spends more than 8 hours each day with his or her rear glued to a desk chair, car seat, or couch, according to the American College of Sports Medicine.

Here's the problem: Just like a car that idles so long its engine stalls, your metabolism puts on the brakes when you lead a sedentary lifestyle, explains James A. Levine, MD, PhD, professor of medicine at the Mayo Clinic. The moment you go from walking slowly to sitting, your active calorie-burn rate drops from roughly 3 per minute to 1. Meanwhile, your triglyceride and blood sugar levels rise. Over time, sitting for hours every day causes your levels of "good" cholesterol (HDL) to fall and puts you at risk of weight gain, diabetes, heart disease, and a variety of cancers.

YOUR POUND-MELTING PLAN

Before you go so far as to torch your living room furniture, take heart. While too much couch time can certainly slow your metabolism and bring your scale to a standstill, the reality is that the amount of movement necessary to correct the problem may not be all that much.

Dr. Levine has developed a program called NEAT (non-exercise activity thermogenesis) to combat America's sitting epidemic. All that it requires is for you to rethink your activity habits and find new, more dynamic ways to get through your day, like walking into Starbucks instead of sitting in the drive-thru. They're all relatively simple strategies, and if you move enough, you can offset the danger of all the sitting you can't avoid. Bonus: You can burn up to 1,000 calories a day, without ever setting foot in the gym.

To prove that this too-good-to-be-true fat-loss solution works in the real world, Dr. Levine and Chris Freytag, *Prevention* magazine's resident fitness expert and pro trainer, ran a test panel on the principles of NEAT. They armed 25 women with a wearable device called the Gruve, which monitors personal activity level and tracks calorie burn (learn more on page 16).

The challenge was simple: The women were told to maximize their daily movements and add mini boosts of activity whenever and wherever possible to burn a mega amount of calories every 24 hours.

The results were astonishing: In just 4 weeks of following a 1,600-calorie-a-day diet and maximizing the incidental activity of their days, the women lost a combined 99 pounds, with some dropping up to 11 pounds, or almost 3 pounds per week. Here are the steps they followed that helped them go from chubby couch potatoes to

muffin-top-blasting moving maniacs—and here's how you can, too.

STEP 1: Calculate Your Calories

Wear an activity monitor (*Prevention*'s test panelists wore the Gruve; see page 16) for 1 week to determine your baseline activity level and daily calorie burn before moving on to Steps 2 and 3. This will help you gauge how much—or how little—you're currently moving, and help you discover where you can make small changes that'll add up to big results.

STEP 2: Start Moving More

After learning how many calories you typically burn in a day, aim to up that number by at least 500 for the next 4 weeks. This will result in an average weight loss of 1 pound per week. Challenge yourself to find creative ways to change your regular patterns (see below for 100 inspiring ideas), and stick with those that work best for your lifestyle.

STEP 3: Fight Fat with Food

The focus of this program is to make healthier choices all day long, and mealtimes are no exception. Follow a 1,600-calorie-a-day diet that's packed with fruits, vegetables, lean proteins, and fewer refined sugars and processed foods. You'll have just the right amount of energy to fuel everyday activities and keep hunger at bay while speeding up weight loss. Chapter 4 will provide you with plenty of tools, so turn to page 29 if you're ready to dive in.

100 WAYS TO STAND UP FOR YOUR HEALTH

We've thought of 100 easy ways you can incorporate more activity into your daily routine without going to the gym. Pick and choose which ones will work best for you. Better yet, try one a week and see how long you can keep it up.

Around the House

1. Hide your remote. If you must watch TV, at least stand up to change the channel.

2. Preset the timer on your TV to turn off after an hour to remind you to do something more active.

3. Slide a small trampoline under your couch and pull it out for *Real Housewives* marathons.

4. Stand up and march during your favorite TV shows.

5. Take each family member's laundry upstairs separately.

6. When tidying up, put things away in multiple small trips rather than one big haul.

7. Help your kids clean their rooms.

8. Organize a closet.

9. Paint, hang curtains, or finish any other home improvement task on your to-do list.

10. Leave your cell phone in one location so that when you need it, you must go to it.

11. Rather than yell toward family members in other rooms, walk over to talk.

12. Walk around your home, yard, or neighborhood while on the phone.

13. Stand while styling your hair and putting on makeup.

14. Wash your car instead of taking it through the car wash.

15. Start a compost pile in your yard.

16. Rake the leaves as a family.

17. Give the delivery guy a break. When you order food in, pick it up yourself.

18. Take a shower instead of a bath.

19. Give your dog a bath instead of paying someone else to do it.

20. Walk to the mailbox instead of checking the mail from your car.

21. Plant or weed a garden or care for indoor plants.

22. Ask for the paper to be left at the end of your driveway instead of by your front door.

23. Instead of sitting and reading, listen to books on tape as you walk, clean, or garden.

24. Put up more Christmas lights.

25. When it snows, shovel your neighbor's sidewalk as well as your own—you'll up your karma, too.

In the Kitchen

26. Chop fresh vegetables instead of buying frozen ones.

27. When cooking or baking, ditch the hand mixer and use a wooden spoon instead.

28. Invest in quality pots and pans. The heavier they are, the more energy it'll take to use them.

29. Hand-wash dishes instead of using the dishwasher.

30. Put most-used items on top or bottom shelves so you have to reach for them.

31. Turn on tunes and dance while cooking.

At Work

32. Drink lots of water. (You'll stand up for refills and trips to the bathroom.)

33. Hover just above your chair in a squat position for 15 seconds every hour.

34. Keep a small water glass, which you must refill often, instead of a large water bottle on your desk.

35. Stand up each time you talk on the phone.

36. Schedule meetings to take place in far-off conference rooms.

37. Buy a plant for your office—watering it will make you more active.

38. Set your computer alarm to ring hourly—stand up for 1 to 5 minutes each time it goes off.

39. Walk outside and eat al fresco or walk to another location in the building instead of sitting and eating at your desk.

40. Invest in a standing desk like the Ergotron WorkFit-S ($379; ergotron.com)—or get crafty and raise your monitor and keyboard with books.

41. Purchase an under-desk pedaling machine, like the Stamina 15-0125 InStride Folding Cycle ($70; staminaproducts.com).

42. Brainstorm while walking.

43. Dust your office weekly.

44. Walk around the block once midmorning and once midafternoon.

45. Make friends with someone on another floor and visit her often.

46. Stand while you open and read your mail.

47. Wear comfortable shoes (or keep flats under your desk) so you walk more.

48. Get rid of your garbage can and walk trash to the kitchen bin.

49. Use the vending machine three floors up and take the stairs.

50. Swap your desk chair for a stability ball and gently bounce on it as you work.

51. When sitting, draw in your ab muscles and tap your toes.

52. Place your stapler far enough away that you have to stand up to get it.

53. Put people on speakerphone and pace around your office during conference calls.

54. If you're meeting a client for drinks, suggest standing at the bar instead of sitting at a table.

55. Invest in a treadmill desk like the TrekDesk ($589; trekdesk.com).

56. Instead of a sit-down meeting, ask your boss if you can "talk and walk."

Traveling

57. When you're waiting for a flight, toss your carry-on in a locker and tour the airport.

58. Skip the moving sidewalks in the terminal.

59. Stand while waiting for a train.

60. When stopping for a road-trip break, take a quick lap around the parking lot.

61. Carpool. On days you don't drive, fidget as much as possible.

62. Get off the bus two stops sooner and walk the rest of the way.

63. Book hotel rooms on a high floor and walk up.

Running Errands

64. If you're buying only a few items, skip the cart and carry a basket.

65. "Waist dance" to the radio or tap out a beat on the steering wheel while driving.

66. Bag your own groceries.

67. Do a few biceps curls each time you pick up shopping bags.

68. Visit a store instead of shopping online.

69. Walk between stores that are in close proximity (don't drive).

70. When picking up your kids from school, get out of the car and greet them with a hug instead of waiting in the car curbside.

71. Skip waiting rooms. When you have an appointment, check in and then head out for a walk until the receptionist phones you.

72. Take a lap around the grocery store before you start shopping.

Just for Fun

73. Get coffee with friends "to go" and walk as you talk and sip.

74. Pick your own apples, strawberries, or other fruits and veggies.

75. Go for a hike.

76. Have sex.

77. Give your sweetie a massage (then have him return the favor).

78. Paint your own toenails instead of sitting for a pedicure.

79. Host a party—the cleaning and prep work will keep you off the couch.

80. Plan active dates with your spouse, such as bowling or golfing, instead of dinner and a movie.

81. Play Frisbee with your kids.

82. Get your book group to slip on sneakers and chat on the move.

83. Play fetch with your dog.

84. Build a snowman.

85. Tour a winery instead of just buying another bottle.

86. Volunteer to deliver meals or help build housing.

87. Go window-shopping or antiquing.

88. Visit a museum or art gallery.

89. Go out dancing or take dancing lessons.

90. Enroll in an active art class, such as sculpture or ceramics.

91. Teach your kids your favorite sport (or have them teach you theirs).

92. Go shopping for new clothes—wriggling into 10 pairs of skinny jeans will get your heart rate up.

93. Cut down your own Christmas tree.

94. Go Christmas caroling with the kids.

95. Buy standing-room-only tickets for sporting events—you'll save cash, too.

96. Do away with chairs at your next cocktail party. Standing will keep everyone mingling.

97. Go camping.

98. Spend the day on the slopes.

99. Join your kids when they break out the Wii instead of just watching.

100. Play backyard games, like badminton, bocce ball, croquet, or kickball.

Lose While You Snooze!

Think that your waking hours are the only time that impacts your weight? Think again.

You may have noticed that falling asleep with the light on leaves you feeling less rested in the morning, but you are probably unaware that it can hinder your weight loss efforts, too. In fact, constant exposure to light disrupts sleep patterns and it puts you at risk of weight *gain*.

Mice exposed to regular light/dark cycles—16 hours of bright light and 8 hours of darkness—gained 50 percent less weight than mice that were exposed to more light. Not clocking enough dark minutes daily also suppresses the sleep hormone melatonin, which your body produces only when it's dark. Any light—whether it's from the TV or the bathroom down the hall—will slow or stop its flow. Here are three smart ways to guarantee your body gets the darkness it needs.

1. Install room-darkening shades or curtains to keep your bedroom as dark as possible.

2. Wear a sleep mask to keep out unwelcome light.

3. Block blue light. The blue spectrum of light is primarily responsible for shutting down melatonin production. Replace regular bulbs in your bedroom and bathroom with low-blue bulbs to cut your exposure (find them at lowbluelights.com).

The Right Yoga for You

Yoga, another no-sweat weight loss solution, is the epitome of mind over muscle: Holding those twisty balanced poses takes strength and flexibility, certainly, but even more critical is the ability to stay focused and concentrate. All types of yoga can help you learn this practice of "being in the moment." What's different from style to style is pace, intensity, and degree of spirituality. Use this guide to choose which of the most popular types of yoga best suits you.

	Vinyasa	Restorative	Kundalini	Iyengar	Bikram	Ashtanga
SWEAT FACTOR:						
	8 out of 10	2 out of 10	5 out of 10	6 out of 10	10 out of 10	7 out of 10
WHAT TO EXPECT:						
	A continuous flow of movements. Most classes move fast (think Power Yoga), but there are also gentle "slow flow" classes.	Relaxing poses that you do lying down with support from blankets or bolsters.	A focus on breath, nontraditional movements, and Eastern philosophy.	A slow class that focuses on alignment by having you hold poses for several minutes.	Twenty-six poses done in 105°F heat (this isn't "hot yoga," which is Vinyasa flow in a hot room).	A fast-paced, athletic practice that links each movement to an inhalation or exhalation.
YOUR FIRST CLASS:						
	Expect tunes, something other styles mostly shun.	You'll rest in each pose for several minutes. You may be led through a guided meditation.	Expect gongs, instructors in white apparel, and an emphasis on balancing the body's energy.	Be ready to break down all the poses and focus on proper form, which can help prevent injury.	The heat will help you stretch. Use the mirrors to make sure you're in the right position.	In an authentic Ashtanga class, you memorize the series and go at your own pace.

Vinyasa	Restorative	Kundalini	Iyengar	Bikram	Ashtanga
TRY IT IF . . .					
You want your mat to stand in for a dance floor.	Stress is keeping you up at night or giving you headaches.	You want a spiritual experience as well as a workout.	You're a perfectionist—with this style, exactitude is key.	You like pushing your body to extremes—and sweating buckets.	You are looking for a calorie-burning workout and enjoy routine.
AVOID IT IF . . .					
You're a beginner. Most instructors expect you to know the poses.	Your goal is weight loss.	Chatting about chakras makes you roll your eyes.	You get antsy if you aren't always moving.	You are sensitive to heat, have high blood pressure or heart disease, or are nursing an injury.	You like variety and being led by an instructor.
OM FACTOR					
Varies from strictly posing to several minutes of chanting.	You may say a few oms, but mainly you'll sit with your thoughts.	Classes usually contain lots of philosophy and singing.	Expect some spirituality woven in, and usually a couple of oms.	All instructors teach from the same script, which doesn't include any oms or philosophy.	Classes may include meditation. Ashtanga is self-practice, so the focus is internal.

Beyond the Pedometer

Ready to kiss your love (seat) handles goodbye? Here are three gadgets that'll help banish chair chub.

STRIIV
($99; striiv.com)
This touch-screen device monitors distance and calorie burn and keeps you motivated with games powered by your movement.

GRUVE *($179.95; gruve.com)*
This multifunctional device senses the intensity and calorie burn of non-exercise activities, such as walking to the copier. As you close in on your daily movement goal, a light changes from red to yellow to green. Plus, it vibrates when you've been sitting for a long time.

BODYMEDIA FIT CORE ARMBAND
($179.95; bodymedia.com)
This armband monitors the calories you burn with every movement through four unique sensors, records your sleep duration and efficiency, and lets you track your progress online.

VITAL STATS

POUNDS LOST: 113
AGE: 47
WEIGHT THEN:
225 pounds
WEIGHT NOW:
112 pounds

Lynn Greenhalge's scale struggles began at age 27, after the birth of her third child. "Between work and chauffeuring the kids, I didn't have time to lose the baby weight," she says. By 2006, at age 42, she weighed 225 pounds.

Her lowest moment came when she realized she barely fit into a size 16. "I dreaded shopping, so I squeezed into embarrassingly tight pants for my son's high school graduation."

However, she soon found that yoga plus portion control was the key to her weight loss success. "Yoga helped me reconnect with my body," recalls Greenhalge, who began practicing twice a week in the fall of 2006. Next, she signed up for Weight Watchers Online and began walking 30 minutes, two or three times a week. By the end of the year, she'd dropped 30 pounds.

In 2008, to blast through a plateau, she upped her cardio: Daily 5:00 a.m., 60-minute walking and running intervals on a treadmill in her bedroom torched calories as her husband snoozed. In fact, Greenhalge was so dedicated to her early morning routine that she wore her workout clothes to bed to make it easier to stay on track. "I sleep in a sports bra. When I get up, I'm exercising." Within 8 months, she'd lost another 50 pounds.

Most importantly, she learned along the way how to make her own success a priority. "I'll forgo my workout to take a walk with my family, but not to watch TV with them. I've worked too hard not to put myself first." Her total weight loss, which she has kept off for more than 2 years, is 113 pounds.

IT WORKED FOR ME
113 Pounds Lost!
Lynn Greenhalge, 47, Webster, Massachusetts

CHAPTER

3

Evaluating Your Progress

WHEN YOU TAKE A long drive to a familiar city, do you always consult a road map? For most of us, as long as we keep seeing the name of our destination popping up in road signs every few miles or so, we remain assured that we're headed in the right direction.

And for many people trying to lose weight, just about the same basic level of reassurance is required. As long as the numbers on the scale keep going down, it's easy to assume all is well. However, road bumps can occur along the weight loss journey, so let this chapter be your first line of defense for troubleshooting the possible wrong turns ahead and finding some new ways to navigate the path that works best for you.

WHY YOUR WEIGHT LOSS PLAN MAY NOT BE WORKING

Odds are that once your weight loss plans are in full swing, you will reach a point where your weekly check-in with the scale shows your weight loss has lost momentum. However, it's important to realize that the fact those numbers are not budging may not have anything to do with your willpower. In fact, some of the most common mistakes people make when they're trying to lose weight may surprise you.

If you find yourself in such a situation, review this chapter carefully. We've assembled a list of questions to help you examine your strategy and get back on track.

Are you eating enough? You may need to bump up your calories to stoke your metabolism. When you dip below about 1,200 calories per day, not only are you not eating enough to get all your nutrients, but also your body slows its metabolism in order to hold onto precious calories, says Christine Gerbstadt, MD, RD, author of *Doctor's Detox Diet*. Also, if you skip meals, your body could lose its ability to feel full. Blame evolution, which has designed our bodies to resist famine and not the buffet table. For example, if you skip breakfast, your body assumes food is scarce. You need a morning meal to let your body know it's okay to burn calories. "Within 1 hour of waking, you should consume a 350- to 500-calorie breakfast, with 10 to 15 grams of protein and fiber to stoke the metabolic fire," says Dr. Gerbstadt.

Do you abstain all day but pig out at night? Even if you are able to eat virtuously during the day, it could be that you're the Jekyll and Hyde of snacking—restricting calories so much by day that by night you're ravenous. After dinner, you trek back and forth to the fridge. Before you know it, you're cuddled up on the couch with a sleeve of Oreos. Start with a breakfast that's really satisfying, like steel-cut oats, eggs, or Greek yogurt. Then at lunch, combine healthy carbs, protein, and fat. And truly savor your treats. Dean Ornish, MD, author of *The Spectrum*, recommends a "chocolate meditation": Take a single piece of the best chocolate you can find and let it dissolve slowly in your mouth, paying attention to the complex flavors. You'll get more pleasure with fewer calories.

Do you reward yourself with food after exercise? Burning 300 calories during a workout is cause for celebration, but rewarding yourself with a high-calorie treat doesn't add up to weight loss. You're likely to overestimate how much the workout burned off and underestimate how much you ate. "Even if you're just working out for well-being, you still have to keep calories in check," says Heidi Skolnik, author of *Nutrient Timing for Peak Performance*.

Have you been consuming a lot of diet drinks? Research suggests that diet drinks may backfire. The taste of something sweet without the calories can cause your body to hold onto calories as fat. In a 2011 study at the University of Texas Health Science Center in San Antonio, diet-soda drinkers had a 178 percent greater increase in waist circumference over 10 years, compared with non-diet-soda drinkers. "Artificial sweeteners can actually raise your insulin levels and lower your blood sugar, which may stimulate hunger and move existing calories into storage in your fat cells," says Sharon P. Fowler, MPH, one of the study's coauthors. Plus, fake sweeteners may not quell a craving like real sugar can because sugar triggers a longer dopamine release. So even after downing two Diet Cokes, you may still want the candy bar.

Are your friends overweight, too? Your chances of being overweight or obese increase half a percent with every friend in your network who is obese, finds a November 2010 study from Harvard University. Even if that friend lives thousands of miles away, your chances of gaining weight still go up, according to a 2007 *New England Journal of Medicine* study. That may be because your perception of being overweight changes—living larger seems acceptable since the heavy person is a friend. (Interestingly, having an obese neighbor that you don't know does not raise your risk.)

Experts also think that a person's lifestyle and behaviors can subconsciously rub off on those in the individual's inner circle. But you don't have to ditch overweight friends to lose weight. In fact, if you embark together on an exercise plan, you can increase your fun and calorie burn: Research from the University of Oxford finds that exercising with friends as a team can actually make the agony of exertion less intense. The same hormones that are released during social bonding, endorphins, also help suppress pain. And once a friend starts to lose weight, you have a greater chance of losing as well (the mechanisms work both ways).

Have you eliminated wine from your diet? New research from Brigham and Women's Hospital in Boston found that women who drank one to two glasses of wine daily gained less weight over 13 years, compared with those women who did not drink alcohol—8 pounds versus 5$\frac{1}{2}$ pounds, to be exact. Of course, if you have other reasons for not drinking, this is no reason to start. But a 5-ounce glass of white wine has on average about 121 calories, so an occasional indulgence is certainly not going to cause you to tip the scales and may even help swing your numbers in the right direction.

Are you keeping your diet low-tech? You may already know that writing down what you eat helps you automatically reduce your calorie intake simply by making you aware of each bite. But did you know that using a digitized program or application with positive feedback could help you lose even more? A new study from the University of Pittsburgh found that people who monitored their diets and exercise with digital devices that provided daily feedback lost more weight and stuck with their diets longer than those who used paper and pen. Not only that, but the high-tech group increased their fruit and veggie intake more than paper users. And you don't have to log in daily or even weekly to benefit. One study found that dieters who recorded meals online just once a month were three times more likely to keep off pounds over 2 years,

compared with those who did so less frequently.

Have you gone no-carb or fat free? Cutting back markedly on any one food group—say, carbs or fat—can leave you short on the nutrients you need to stay energized. One study found that dieters low in calcium and vitamin C had higher odds of putting on belly fat. The trick is a varied diet that includes healthy fats and good carbs such as fruits. After all, the biggest reason low-carb diets backfire is that, for the vast majority of people, they aren't sustainable over the long haul. It's a rare soul who can pass up birthday cake and pasta dinners for a lifetime. And as with all diets, once you quit, you regain the weight you lost and (often) more. These fluctuations can make it an even bigger challenge to lose weight next time.

GETTING BACK ON TRACK

So if you've veered off course a little bit in your weight loss efforts, what else can you do to make sure you stay headed in the right direction? Consider one (or more) of these five strategies to help you redefine a new starting point.

Start first thing in the morning. You know the expression "well begun is half done"? So it is with your weight loss efforts. If you dash out the door without eating breakfast, you're likely to return home a little heavier than you need to be. A study from the University of Massachusetts Medical School showed that people who skip breakfast are $4\frac{1}{2}$ times more likely to be obese than breakfast eaters. One possible reason: Going hungry first thing in the day can slow your metabolism—your body's fat-burning engine—by up to 10 percent, according to the University of Pittsburgh Medical Center.

Don't use the "D word." As we've already discussed in Chapter 1, some experts think that we have a tendency to get hung up when we rely on the idea of a "diet" as a means to weight loss. Just by going on a diet, you make it inevitable that one day you'll go off that diet. Deprivation simply doesn't work as a weight loss technique. You may be able to stick with a starvation program for a couple of weeks or months, but sooner or later your body's cravings will kick in, and when that happens, you'll be having a close encounter with a bucket of fried chicken.

So rather than giving your life a complete overhaul, try instituting a series of small changes you can stick with. If they become lifestyle habits—taking a walk after dinner every night, eating a good breakfast each morning—they will benefit you in the long run. And while incremental change may mean slower progress initially, the payoff is that you'll enjoy greater long-term success.

Downsize your stress. There's a scary connection between stress and food: When you feel stressed, your body produces a hormone called cortisol, a powerful hunger inducer. When the bills pile up on your desk and your work trip coincides with your babysitter's vacation, you may feel compelled to rip open the box of chocolate chip cookies you bought "for the kids." Worse yet, that same hormone can cause your body to store fat.

Because the effect of stress on your appetite is so profound, try to manage your false-appetite triggers by doing something different when you feel the urge to snack. Take a walk, drink a glass of water, watch a funny video on YouTube, or call a friend. Finding some good ways to dodge sweets and sodas can make a major dent in your calorie intake and help you cope better with stress, too. A Tufts University study found that eating carbs could increase levels of anxiety, so those cookies and sweet drinks you think will help you through the stress points might actually be having the opposite effect.

Kiss cravings goodbye. In the time it took you to read those words, you've probably already conjured an image of your favorite gooey dessert, with a well-laden spoon hovering in your mind's eye. Go ahead and admire it, and definitely give in on special occasions. But the rest of the time, find ways to manage those temptations. As many successful weight loss winners can attest, one of the best ways to handle cravings is to keep your energy supply steady so that you're not tempted by the fast-food jungle.

Most people also find that it's easier to beat a craving if you can avoid having it in the first place. To do that, eat on a schedule. Experts generally advise eating five times a day: breakfast, lunch, and dinner, plus two healthy snacks to tide you over in between. What kind of snacks? Combine a piece of fruit and a piece of cheese, spread some whole wheat crackers with peanut butter, have a handful of nuts with a glass of milk, or stir blueberries into a cup of yogurt. If you keep to your meal-and-snack plan, your energy levels will remain steady and your cravings will vanish. Really.

Buy some new dishes. The increase in portion sizes has made national news. It's not uncommon now to find restaurant entrées that tip the scales at 3,000 calories. But there's another trend you may not be aware of. Our plates are growing as well, according to the food scientists at Cornell University. And many of us were taught to clean our plates when we were growing up; for some it was perhaps the only nutrition rule we ever knew. But here's the problem: If we're all cleaning our plates, as they grow larger, we do, too.

Take a look through your cabinets and replace the largest dinner platters with smaller ones. As your dishware shrinks, your portion sizes grow smaller. While you're at it, follow another piece of advice from the food science labs at Cornell: Never eat out of the bag or carton. A study showed that the bigger the popcorn bag given to moviegoers, the more they would eat. Dole out a moderate scoop of ice cream or you'll weigh as much as Ben & Jerry . . . combined.

HOW TO AVOID THREE SERIOUS SNACK TRAPS

We do it in the car, on the train, in front of the TV, on the phone, and even in bed. For too many of us, snacking has become so automatic that our brains barely register the hand-to-mouth motion. And it's not as if we're all reaching for diet-friendly apples: A 2010 study from the University of North Carolina found that most of us eat nearly 600 calories a day—roughly a third of our food—in snacks rather than meals. Here are three common places most of us get into trouble—and how you can avoid their pitfalls.

You Can't Stop Eating in the Car

If you feel like you live in your car, you probably consume a lot of calories there, too. Maybe you wolf down snacks straight out of the bag, with little idea of how much you've inhaled, or you pull into the nearest drive-thru for a shake.

Pack portable, calorie-controlled nibbles such as small bags of cashews or an apple to preempt unrestrained noshing. Even half of a PB&J on whole wheat will do the trick. And if those fries are still calling out to you, "drive home via another route so you won't pass your favorite fast-food restaurants," says Janna L. Fikkan, PhD, a health psychologist at Duke Integrative Medicine. "It doesn't have to be the shortest way home, as long as you avoid the drive-thru."

You Work at Home

It's just you and the fridge—and nobody watching. Because you have no meetings or structured activities, you can check the mail, toss in a load of laundry, play with the dog—and grab a snack (or two or four).

Keep a log of your daily activities, including every time you get up to eat. Chances are, once you see how often you're indulging, you'll be shamed into cutting back. If you still feel the need to snack, sit at the kitchen table and don't do anything else while you eat. Without the distraction of the computer, TV, or newspaper, you'll be much more aware of how often you eat out of habit rather than hunger.

You Graze at the Office

Between the office candy bowl, the vending machine, and a co-worker's homemade brownies, your office probably stocks more snacks than a 7-Eleven. And since you're only nibbling, the calories don't count, right?

Bring in healthy snacks and launch a counteroffensive. Pick something delicious—tamari-roasted almonds or dark chocolate, perhaps—that you actually prefer over the junk. Knowing that these treats are tucked away will give you the strength to resist the disastrous jelly doughnuts. If you know ahead of time that you won't be able to leave your desk at noon, brown-bag it for lunch. With healthy fare within arm's reach, you won't need to raid your colleague's candy jar.

Seven Snacks Under 100 Calories

SNACK 1
2 (6") corn tortillas +
2 tablespoons salsa

SNACK 2
1 cup pineapple chunks +
2 teaspoons shredded coconut

SNACK 3
25 pistachios

SNACK 4
½ cup Cheerios +
½ cup fat-free milk

SNACK 5
½ cup 0% honey Greek yogurt

SNACK 6
A handful (⅛ cup) of dry-roasted pumpkin seeds

SNACK 7
5 fresh apricots

IT WORKED FOR ME

110 Pounds Lost!

Catherine Zanoni, 46, Brentwood, Tennessee

IT WORKED FOR ME

78 Pounds Lost!

Aldith Diaz, 52, Nashville

VITAL STATS

POUNDS LOST: 110
AGE: 46
WEIGHT THEN:
247 pounds
WEIGHT NOW:
137 pounds

VITAL STATS

POUNDS LOST: 78
AGE: 52
WEIGHT THEN:
198 pounds
WEIGHT NOW:
120 pounds

At times during each of her three pregnancies, from ages 21 to 27, Catherine Zanoni felt like she wasn't just eating for two—it was like she was eating for 12. "I ate with abandon," she says. "I'd eat a pint of Häagen-Dazs in one sitting." Zanoni gained about 60 pounds with each pregnancy, eventually tipping the scale at 247 pounds. A string of diets over the next 15 years still left her at 217.

Aldith Diaz, whose childhood chub earned her the nickname Butterball by age 5, can relate. Although she lost about 30 pounds when she married at age 26, she put the weight back on with each of her three pregnancies, weighing 198 pounds by age 34. "All I wanted to do was eat and sleep," she recalls.

Both women describe their lowest moment as the time when they realized that they were too tired to live their own lives. "I couldn't believe that reflection in the mirror was me," Zanoni says. "I felt hopeless." Diaz remembers listening to her kids tear through the house while she lay on the couch, too tired to stop them. "It just took too much effort," she explains.

Both devout Christians, Zanoni and Diaz were drawn to the Weigh Down Method (WDM), which uses biblical teachings and a spiritual emphasis to help participants become more mindful about their eating habits rather than approaching diets as a mathematical equation. One of the main goals: switching the focus from food to faith. "I used to deal with my stress by plowing through a pan of brownies," says Zanoni, who began strictly following the WDM in 2001 because it doesn't force a prescribed set of food rules or preach regular exercise. "Now, when I feel stressed, I pray instead," she says. Over the next 2 years, she lost 110 pounds and has kept the weight off for more than 9 years.

Diaz, who dropped 30 pounds on a 30-day juice fast in February 1998, knew she needed to find a more sustainable way to reach her goal weight and began the WDM a few weeks later. Within a year of following the principles, Diaz dropped 50 pounds. "I ate only when my stomach growled and stopped when I was satisfied," says Diaz. Now she has maintained a 78-pound weight loss for 12 years and gone from a size 22 to a size 4.

What to Eat (and When)

AS WE'VE ALREADY DISCUSSED, weight gain and obesity are big problems in our society, and it's not entirely our fault. We live in an environment where food is supersized, and most of us eat more calories than our bodies need. In fact, in 2007 the average American ate close to 2,800 calories per day, compared with about 2,200 in 1970, according to the USDA's Economic Research Service. That daily difference can add up to an extra pound of body fat every week.

Growing portion sizes are partially to blame. When plates, packages, and portions are larger, we eat more, explains Cornell University professor Brian Wansink, PhD, in a 2007 study published in the *Journal of the American Dietetic Association*. Even cookbook portions have been upsized: A recent study in the *Annals of Internal Medicine* found a

42 percent increase in recipe portion size since 1931. (A portion is the amount of food that you serve yourself, while a serving is the measured amount recommended on the label that contains the displayed number of calories.)

Not only are we presented with giant piles of food at every turn, but also most of us don't even know the basics: how many calories we need or consume. In a study in the *American Journal of Public Health*, close to 200 survey respondents who were asked to estimate the calories and fat in nine restaurant entrées were off by more than 100 percent—they thought that a meal with more than 1,300 calories had only 642 calories.

So how exactly should you approach the calorie question if weight loss is your goal? After all, we've already covered how the "D word" can set us up for disaster. To tackle the issue of portion size, we've developed a handy chart that helps you recognize what an appropriate serving looks like without relying on weights and measures all the time. We've also put together a helpful guide to buying fruits and vegetables at the peak of freshness. But before we go into all of that, first let's start by thinking about what you're putting on your plate in the first place. Let's consider the simple strategy of going green.

HOW THINKING GREEN CAN LEAD TO LEAN

Not so long ago, professional chefs and harried moms alike seemed to lavish most of their culinary efforts on the item at the center of their dinner plates—the inevitable hunk of meat. Vegetables were an afterthought, perfectly adequate for a side dish but rarely the centerpiece and certainly not the most exciting part of the meal. But after years of playing supporting roles, veggies are starting to share the spotlight and, in some venues at least, are even becoming the new divas of dinner.

This quiet revolution can be seen in the growing number of popular veggie-centric cookbooks, restaurants, diet plans, and gorgeous supermarket displays that transform the produce section of many groceries into a garden of delights. (Eataly, a New York City market, even has a "vegetable butcher," who will do the chopping for you on demand.) The reason for this new push is no mystery. "Research has consistently shown that people who eat larger proportions of fruits and vegetables—particularly vegetables—are healthier," says Marion Nestle, PhD, professor of nutrition, food studies, and public health at New York University.

You don't need to be fully vegetarian or vegan to reap the health benefits. But you do need to consume more vegetables—not spinach pasta or veggie chips but actual whole vegetables. The key is just to flip the ratio of foods in your diet. "Instead of an 8-ounce steak and a 4-ounce portion of vegetables, serve 4 ounces of beef and 8 ounces of veggies," advises Michael Pollan in the new edition of his bestseller *Food Rules*. Equally important, eat fewer processed foods while increasing those vegetable servings. As Pollan puts it: "If it came from a plant, eat it. If it was made in a plant, don't."

Restaurants have gotten the message and are amping up their veggie options—and many are finding that it's good for the bottom line. When Andrew Weil, MD (a member of *Prevention* magazine's editorial advisory board), opened True Food Kitchen in Phoenix in 2008, his restaurant partner and CEO, Sam Fox, was doubtful that the veggie-rich venture would succeed. Now there are three additional locations—in Scottsdale, Arizona; Santa Monica, California; and Newport Beach, California—and plans to open four more this year in San Diego, Boston, Denver, and Houston. "Sam says he's never seen anything like it," says Dr. Weil. "There are diners who come in four or five times a week. People come up to him on the street and hug him."

Of course, it's one thing to let a chef do all the work and quite another to do your own washing, peeling, and chopping. But with grocery stores stocking more prechopped fresh and ready-to-cook frozen veggies, raising your vegetable quotient has never been easier. The simplest approach, says Mark Bittman, author of *Food Matters* and *How to Cook Everything Vegetarian*, is to change the proportions of ingredients in dishes you cook anyway. "Make frittatas with more vegetables and fewer eggs," he suggests. "Instead of cassoulet that's heavy on meat and light on vegetables, prepare it with lots of beans and veggies and just a little meat for flavor and texture."

Or, if you're willing to put in a touch more effort, you can turn your veggies into gourmet fare. "The range of possibilities is far greater with vegetables than with meat," says Daniel Patterson, chef-owner of the trendy restaurant Coi in San Francisco. "I could give you 500 flavors of plants. You can't get 500 flavors of meat."

To discover your own new tastes, turn to page 193 for an entire chapter dedicated to meatless meals, but don't overlook the many vegetarian options sprinkled throughout some of the other chapters as well. You'll find plenty of spice in dishes like the Caribbean Tofu and Veggie Sandwiches on page 74 or the Meatless Tacos on page 229, as well as recipes that will ensure you'll hardly miss the meat, like the Wild Mushroom-Lentil Burgers on page 95.

How to Enjoy the Right Amounts

Another important way you can make sure the calorie equation is working in your favor is to pay close attention to portion sizes. Of course, it's not always easy. Estimating food portions and calories can be tough, no matter how many diets you've been on. And estimating ingredient amounts rather than measuring when you're cooking can sabotage your good intentions—just one extra tablespoon of oil in a dish is hardly noticeable in terms of texture and flavor, but it can add 120 calories to the finished product.

So that's why we've tried to make it easier for you with our handy visual reference guide on page 33. While you will still need to measure out ingredients for each recipe, learning how the visual cues correspond to actual weights and measures can also help you see your options through a new lens. Once you're in the habit of seeing what an appropriate serving of beans looks like, for example, the entire process will become easier, though it's still a good idea to check yourself now and then to make sure your portion sizes are still in line with these guidelines.

Fortunately, you don't need any special

gadgets or gizmos. Instead, we've provided you with some common visual references, such as a golf ball or the palm of your hand, to eyeball correct amounts of food. You'll notice that alongside these visual cues are some volume measurements (teaspoons, tablespoons, and cups), which are the easiest way to visualize most foods. But some foods, such as chips and pretzels, as well as meat, poultry, and fish, are awkward shapes and don't fit neatly into either a real or imaginary spoon or cup. You'll usually see such foods measured by weight. Also, we've listed 4 ounces here as a serving size for meat, poultry, or fish, even though the most frequently recommended serving size for meat is 3 ounces. It's not a mistake: 4 ounces refers to the raw weight, 3 ounces to the cooked weight. For more details on how weight measurements match up to volume measurements, see the Conversion Chart on the last page of this book.

Sure, weighing and measuring meals isn't terribly fun—plus, it's sometimes inconvenient, potentially boring, and tough to keep up for more than a couple of days. But it is the most accurate way to tell how much food you're eating.

Your Guide to Great Produce

One of the most significant things we can do to keep our weight loss efforts on track is to concentrate on eating fruits and vegetables. But to enjoy everything those foods have to offer, it's important to select, store, and serve them while at the peak of freshness. To help you do just that, we've compiled a list of 10 of the most common fruits and vegetables that still present some challenges when it comes to getting consistent results. Here's what you need to know about buying the best and keeping it that way.

APPLES. These are one of the few fruits grown in all 50 states, so in late fall it's very easy for everyone to find them locally grown and freshly picked. Depending on the variety, taste can range from sweet to tart. Try using a mix of types within a recipe for the best results. To save money, purchase all-purpose Golden Delicious, Granny Smith, or McIntosh, which are good for both cooking and snacking, and buy in bulk. Store apples by themselves in the crisper (they emit ethylene gas, which can wilt or spoil other produce).

Fast fact: Apples get high marks for heart health. They supply fiber, including a soluble type called pectin, and antioxidants and may help lower cholesterol naturally.

ASPARAGUS. Here's a case where size doesn't matter. Thick and thin asparagus spears are equally delicious—provided you

It's a Ball, It's a Hand, It's a Portion

BALL	HAND	PORTION	EXAMPLES
Small marble	Tip of the thumb	1 teaspoon	Oil, butter, margarine, sugar
Large marble	Thumb to the first knuckle	1 tablespoon	Chopped nuts, honey, ketchup
2 large marbles	Whole thumb	2 tablespoons/1 ounce liquid	Salad dressing, grated cheese, raisins
Golf ball	Cupped handful	¼ cup/1 ounce shredded cheese	Beans, chopped vegetables, salsa, hummus
Hockey puck	Palm of the hand	½ cup/4 ounces (¼ pound) raw meat, poultry, fish	Burger patty, beef, pork, chicken, turkey, fish
Tennis ball	Open handful	½ cup	Rice, pasta, fruit salad, melon balls, small roll, scrambled eggs
Wiffle ball	Very loose cupped handful	1 cup/1 to 2 ounces chips	Potato chips, tortilla chips, popcorn, pretzels
Baseball	Whole fist	1 cup	Cereal, lettuce, vegetables, strawberries, soup

enjoy them soon after picking. Buy bright green spears that have tightly closed tips and are uniformly thick (to ensure even cooking). Refrigerate them upright in shallow water for up to 3 days. Before cooking, snap or slice off the woody ends and peel thick stalks, if necessary.

Fast fact: Asparagus supplies inulin, a special fiber that helps the "good" bacteria in your digestive tract.

CABBAGE. The trick for great-tasting cabbage boils down to this: Don't overcook it. Raw cabbage has a mild flavor and adds color and crunch to salads and slaws. A quick sauté or gentle braise makes it pleasantly pungent. But go too far and the bitter, slightly stinky sulfur compounds in this cruciferous vegetable take over. Choose heads without yellowed or wilted leaves. Wrap in plastic wrap and refrigerate for up to a week or two. Cabbage is rich in fiber and antioxidants that may prevent cancer and heart disease.

Fast fact: Red cabbage contains cancer-fighting anthocyanins. Cook it with vinegar to keep its pretty purple hue.

CITRUS. The orange is America's main squeeze, but during the winter we'd do well to develop a wandering eye for other colorful citrus, from the tiny kumquat to the giant pomelo. Buy unblemished fruit, and store it in the fridge for up to 3 weeks. The flesh supplies fiber, while the peel (or zest) contains most of the vitamin C. Grate the peel (wash in hot water first to remove any wax, and avoid catching the bitter white pith) and use immediately to capture the flavorful, aromatic oils.

Fast fact: To get the most juice, bring the fruit to room temperature and roll it between your palm and the counter before squeezing.

CUCUMBERS. Although you can buy these veggies year-round, don't miss the opportunity to take advantage of your locally grown crops in the peak of summer. Choose firm cucumbers with a vibrant green color and avoid any with soft spots. Store them at the front of the fridge, where it's warmer; these water-laden veggies can start to freeze in the colder temperatures of the crisper. Garden-variety cucumbers sold in supermarkets are typically buffed with food-grade wax to preserve freshness (note the shiny exterior) and should be peeled for best taste.

Fast fact: If the skin on your cucumber is dull, eat it. You'll get fiber, vitamin A, and silica, a mineral that's good for your complexion.

EGGPLANT. This veggie has a split personality. Grilled or sautéed briefly, eggplant has a firm, almost meaty texture. But roast it awhile in the oven and you'll be amazed at the creamy, silky result. Most varieties—whether purple, white, or striped—have a mild, earthy taste that melds with other flavors. Before buying, gently squeeze eggplant (they should give a little bit) and check for soft or brown spots. Store in a cool spot outside the fridge for a couple of days. Eggplant sops up oil, so brush or spray it on right before cooking.

Fast fact: Eat the skin to get fiber and cancer-fighting antioxidants.

MUSHROOMS. These fantastic fungi bring meaty texture and complex flavor to dishes for very few calories. Avoid those with dark or wet spots or a mildew smell. Store mushrooms in their original packaging (put loose ones in a paper bag) and refrigerate for up to 3 to 4 days. Rinse them gently and pat dry, or wipe with a damp paper towel, just before using. But never soak them—because mushrooms are so porous, they'll become waterlogged.

Fast fact: Mushrooms exposed to UV light as they grow contain high levels of bone-building vitamin D. Check the packaging to identify these types.

SQUASH. Don't let its pale exterior fool you. Butternut squash is dressed for the fall season with vivid orange flesh, thanks to beta-carotene. Although you can find winter squash during much of the year, they're sweetest just after the fall harvest. Choose heavy, firm, stem-on squash without soft spots. Store them someplace cool and dry and they'll keep for several weeks. Or buy this veggie peeled and cubed to save time and effort. Check the date for freshness and keep chilled.

Fast fact: Serve butternut squash with a little heart-healthy fat, such as olive oil, to get the most of its cancer-fighting antioxidants.

STRAWBERRIES. When picked at their peak, strawberries are luscious, heavenly scented, and red all the way through. And what you see and smell is what you get, as this fruit doesn't continue to ripen after harvest. Choose deeply colored berries and avoid mushy ones. Consider buying organic because strawberries retain a high level of pesticide residue. Chill whole, unwashed berries in a single layer, loosely covered. Just before using, rinse gently in a bowl of cold water (don't run them under the tap) and dry on paper towels (wet berries spoil faster). Then, enjoy.

Fast fact: Strawberries are rich in antioxidants and, ounce for ounce, have more vitamin C than oranges.

ZUCCHINI. In late summer, zucchini are so plentiful that farmers' markets and neighborhood gardeners are practically giving them away. For the best of the bounty, choose smaller vegetables up to the size of a large banana (bigger ones can be tougher).

Fast fact: More than delicious, zucchini contain lutein, a compound that may protect your eyes from cataracts and macular degeneration.

VEGGIES IN A SNAP

Does all the prep work keep you from cooking vegetables? These products offer some easy shortcuts.

Mann's Broccoli Cole Slaw
Pile this crunchy medley of shredded broccoli, carrots, and red cabbage on your burger. Or toss it in a light Asian-style vinaigrette to make slaw.

Glory Foods Kale Greens
This prechopped, prewashed kale is picked when it's young and tender. Steam it, toss in a little oil, and add chopped pine nuts. Season to taste.

Cascadian Farm Premium Blends
Make a 15-minute stir-fry with Chinese-Style Stirfry Blend (green beans, broccoli, carrots, red peppers, onions, and mushrooms). Toss in a wok with soy sauce and sesame oil.

Melissa's Steamed Lentils
Normally, lentils take 25 minutes to an hour to cook. These are ready to eat. Microwave them in minutes for veggie casseroles—or use cold in a salad.

Cooking Beans and Grains

Some of our recipes and meals call for cooked pasta, rice, grains, or beans. Unfortunately, food packages may not provide information on the amount of uncooked grain or beans that you need for a cooked portion. Use this short guide to help you figure out how much is required to make 1 cup cooked.

FOOD	DRY AMOUNT	VOLUME	WEIGHT
Pasta	½ cup	Tennis ball	2 ounces
Rice	⅓ cup	5 large marbles	2⅔ ounces
Couscous	Scant ½ cup	Tennis ball	2½ ounces
Barley	Heaping ¼ cup	Golf ball	2 ounces
Dried beans	Scant ½ cup	Tennis ball	2⅔ ounces

IT WORKED FOR ME

107 Pounds Lost!

Shannon Hammer, 42, Redondo Beach, California

Put on her first diet at the early age of 4 by her family, Shannon Hammer grew up feeling as though her weight was constantly monitored. As a child, she'd rebel by sneaking food—a bite of cake here, a few cookies there—and then covering her tracks. Later, she tried every diet from cabbage soup to grapefruit, but her feelings of anger and shame, coupled with the intense hunger brought on by calorie restriction, led to full-blown binges.

One of her most vivid memories is of finishing off a half-eaten pint of ice cream and running to the corner store to buy a new pint, then eating that to the halfway point to keep her family from discovering her shameful secret. "By the time I was 30, I had tried every diet out there and even had taken laxatives and appetite suppressants—and I still weighed 230 pounds," says Hammer.

One of her lowest moments came when she realized she would continue to eat until the cupboards were bare. "I'd eat whatever was in the

VITAL STATS

POUNDS LOST: 107
AGE: 42
WEIGHT THEN:
230 pounds
WEIGHT NOW:
123 pounds

house—half a loaf of bread, four bowls of cereal. I wouldn't stop until I was panting in pain."

After seeing a photo of herself in January 2001, Hammer, then a size 22, knew things had to change. "I was looking at an obese woman with my face. I was horrified." She started following a low-carb diet, largely because it eliminated sugar and flour, her trigger foods. She began looking at cake, cookies, and pasta the way a recovering alcoholic views a glass of bourbon: as off-limits—forever. In fact, she became diligent about looking at ingredient lists when evaluating her food choices. "Now I always check labels to make sure I avoid sugar."

Hammer also ditched her straight-to-the-plate mentality. "I weigh or measure everything I eat or drink. Practicing portion control is key." And she turns to her journaling habit whenever she feels the need to keep emotional eating in check. "I used to turn to food for comfort, but now I write in my journal when I'm frustrated or worried."

She also began walking almost every day, and, eventually, 20 minutes became 2 hours. Over the next 2 years, she dropped almost 40 pounds. Another 2 years later, exercising nearly an hour a day and controlling her portion sizes, Hammer had shed an additional 70 pounds.

As for keeping her motivation up to maintain her 107-pound weight loss, Hammer credits her fear of backsliding. "I still feel like I'm one bite away from a binge. You can't return to your old habits after you lose the weight. This is a lifestyle that has to continue."

Breakfasts

Strawberry Shortcake Smoothie

One-half cup of strawberries provides more than half of the Daily Value (DV) of vitamin C, a potent antioxidant that boosts production of collagen fibers, which help keep skin smooth and firm.

1 **banana**

1 **cup low-fat vanilla yogurt**

½ **cup sliced strawberries**

¼ **cup vanilla soy milk or 1% milk**

2 **vanilla wafers, crumbled**

COMBINE the banana, yogurt, strawberries, and milk in a food processor or blender and puree until thick and smooth.
Spoon into a glass and sprinkle the wafer crumbs over the top.

TOTAL TIME: 5 minutes **MAKES 1 SERVING**

PER SERVING: 422 calories, 16 g protein, 78 g carbohydrates, 7 g total fat, 3 g saturated fat, 5 g fiber, 227 mg sodium

Melon-Mango Smoothie

Try this fast and refreshing smoothie for a high-energy breakfast that won't leave you feeling loaded down.

- ¾ cup frozen mango chunks
- ½ cup frozen or fresh sliced banana
- ½ cup chopped cantaloupe
- ⅓ cup low-fat vanilla yogurt
- ¼ cup vanilla soy milk or 1% milk
- ¼ cup low-fat granola

COMBINE the mango, banana, cantaloupe, yogurt, and milk in a food processor or blender and puree until thick and smooth. Spoon into a glass and sprinkle the granola over the top.

TOTAL TIME: 5 minutes **MAKES 1 SERVING**

PER SERVING: 372 calories, 10 g protein, 81 g carbohydrates, 4 g total fat, 1 g saturated fat, 7 g fiber, 151 mg sodium

WHY YOU SHOULD CHOOSE

No-salt-added canned tomato products

Canned tomatoes come in many forms for use in soups, stews, casseroles, and sauces. Buy no-salt-added varieties whenever possible so that you can control the salt content.

Super Strawberry Smoothie

Designed for people on the go, this smoothie uses store-bought pomegranate juice. If you prefer to make your own, cut a pomegranate in half and strain the juice in a cheesecloth-lined hand-press juicer.

⅔ cup frozen chopped strawberries

½ cup 0% vanilla Greek yogurt

⅓ cup vanilla soy milk or 1% milk

¼ cup pomegranate juice

COMBINE the strawberries, yogurt, milk, and juice in a food processor or blender and puree until thick and smooth. Spoon into a glass and serve.

TOTAL TIME: 5 minutes **MAKES 1 SERVING**

PER SERVING: 182 calories, 13 g protein, 30 g carbohydrates, 1 g total fat, 0 g saturated fat, 2 g fiber, 86 mg sodium

Maple-Pecan Oatmeal

Research shows that eating oats can lower total and LDL ("bad") cholesterol and help reduce insulin resistance. The soluble fiber contained in oats slows the rate at which your body can break down and absorb carbohydrates, which means your blood sugar levels remain stable.

¼ **cup pecans, chopped**

4 **cups vanilla soy milk or 1% milk, divided**

2 **cups old-fashioned rolled oats**

1 **teaspoon ground cinnamon**

Pinch of salt

2 **tablespoons maple syrup**

TOAST the pecans in a dry skillet over medium-high heat, tossing frequently, until fragrant. Place on a plate and set aside.

COMBINE 3½ cups of the milk, the oats, cinnamon, and salt in a large pot and bring to a boil over medium heat. Reduce the heat and simmer for 5 minutes, or until the oatmeal reaches desired thickness.

DIVIDE the oatmeal among 4 bowls and top each serving with 2 tablespoons of the remaining milk. Drizzle with the maple syrup and sprinkle with the toasted pecans.

TOTAL TIME: 10 minutes **MAKES 4 SERVINGS**

PER SERVING: 90 calories, 14 g protein, 46 g carbohydrates, 10 g total fat, 1 g saturated fat, 5 g fiber, 145 mg sodium

Oats Breakfast Pudding with Dates and Walnuts

This satisfying oatmeal is delicious served hot with milk. If you have leftovers, they're just as tasty served cold with sliced fruit the next day.

3 cups vanilla soy milk or 1% milk

1½ cups quick-cooking oats

½ cup chopped dates

½ cup chopped walnuts

¼ teaspoon apple pie spice

PREHEAT the oven to 325°F. Coat an 8" × 8" glass or ceramic baking dish with cooking spray.

COMBINE the milk, oats, dates, walnuts, and spice in the dish. Stir to mix. Cover with foil.

BAKE for 1 hour, or until thickened and bubbling. Let stand for 10 minutes before serving.

TOTAL TIME: 1 hour 15 minutes **MAKES 8 SERVINGS**

PER SERVING: 351 calories, 12 g protein, 52 g carbohydrates, 12 g total fat, 2 g saturated fat, 6 g fiber, 56 mg sodium

Homemade Granola

Some granola recipes call for a large amount of vegetable oil, but this one takes a more modest approach, which keeps the calories per serving relatively low.

2 cups old-fashioned rolled oats

2 tablespoons firmly packed brown sugar

2 tablespoons honey

2 teaspoons canola oil

1 teaspoon vanilla extract

½ teaspoon ground cinnamon

⅛ teaspoon salt

1 tablespoon ground flaxseeds

¼ cup roasted soy nuts or sunflower seeds

PREHEAT the oven to 350°F.

SPREAD the oats in a single layer on a jelly-roll pan. Bake for 18 minutes, or until toasted, stirring halfway through the baking time.

MEANWHILE, whisk together the sugar, honey, oil, vanilla, cinnamon, and salt in a large bowl. Toss in the hot oats until evenly coated.

COAT the same pan with cooking spray. Spread the granola in an even layer in the pan.

BAKE for 13 to 15 minutes, or until golden brown. Sprinkle the flaxseeds evenly over the top. Cool in the pan on a rack for 30 minutes. Stir in the soy nuts or sunflower seeds. Store in an airtight container.

TOTAL TIME: 1 hour 15 minutes   **MAKES 6 SERVINGS**

PER SERVING: 187 calories, 5 g protein, 30 g carbohydrates, 5 g total fat, 0.5 g saturated fat, 3 g fiber, 50 mg sodium

Unforgettable Grits

These grits complement any weekend breakfast menu, but they're so creamy and delicious you might find them to be the perfect base for a variety of weeknight meals as well.

- **4 cups water**
- **1 teaspoon salt**
- **1 cup quick-cooking grits**
- **½ cup thinly sliced scallions**
- **¼ cup finely chopped roasted red bell pepper**
- **1 cup shredded reduced-fat Cheddar cheese**

COMBINE the water and salt in a large saucepan. Bring to a boil over medium-high heat.

ADD the grits, whisking constantly until the mixture returns to a boil.

REDUCE the heat to low and add the scallions and pepper. Cook, whisking constantly, for 5 minutes, or until the grits are tender and the mixture is thick.

STIR in the cheese and serve when melted.

TOTAL TIME: 15 minutes **MAKES 4 SERVINGS**

PER SERVING: 196 calories, 10 g protein, 32 g carbohydrates, 2 g total fat, 1 g saturated fat, 1 g fiber, 772 mg sodium

Sweet Potato and Sausage Skillet

For heartier appetites, round out the meal with a side of scrambled egg whites.

4 teaspoons olive oil, divided

1 pound precooked chicken-and-apple sausage, cut into ½" diagonal slices

2 large sweet potatoes, peeled, quartered, and cut into ½" wedges

¼ teaspoon ground black pepper

¼ teaspoon dried thyme

2 tablespoons water

2 tablespoons maple syrup

HEAT 2 teaspoons of the oil in a large nonstick skillet over medium heat. Add the sausage and cook, turning often, for 6 minutes, or until lightly browned. Remove from the skillet and set aside.

HEAT the remaining 2 teaspoons oil in the same skillet over medium heat. Add the sweet potatoes, pepper, thyme, and water. Cook, stirring often, for 12 to 14 minutes, or until the potatoes are tender.

RETURN the sausage to the skillet. Add the maple syrup and toss to heat through.

TOTAL TIME: 25 minutes MAKES 4 SERVINGS

PER SERVING: 289 calories, 15 g protein, 26 g carbohydrates, 15 g total fat, 4 g saturated fat, 5 g fiber, 596 mg sodium

Turkey Sausage

To keep this sausage at the ready, shape the patties and freeze on a plastic wrap–lined baking sheet for an hour, or until firm. Transfer to a resealable plastic freezer bag and freeze for up to 2 months. Use the patties for a quick breakfast sandwich, or crumble the bulk sausage to use in other recipes.

½ small onion, grated

2 tablespoons chopped fresh parsley

½ teaspoon ground paprika

¾ teaspoon dried rubbed sage

¾ teaspoon ground black pepper

½ teaspoon salt

¼ teaspoon ground ginger

¼ teaspoon dried oregano

1¼ pounds extra-lean ground turkey

COMBINE the onion, parsley, paprika, sage, pepper, salt, ginger, and oregano in a large bowl. Add the turkey and stir until well blended.

SHAPE into patties 2" in diameter (use 2 slightly rounded tablespoonfuls of the mixture for each patty).

HEAT a large nonstick skillet coated with cooking spray over medium-low heat. Cook the patties for 3 to 4 minutes per side, or until golden brown and cooked through.

TOTAL TIME: 20 minutes **MAKES 5 SERVINGS**

PER SERVING: 127 calories, 28 g protein, 1 g carbohydrates, 2 g total fat, 0 g saturated fat, 1 g fiber, 299 mg sodium

Super-Easy Breakfast Wraps

Even when you're on the go, be sure to eat breakfast. Taking in most of your calories early in the day means you're less likely to overeat or snack in the evening.

- 2 teaspoons olive oil, divided
- 1 cup halved grape tomatoes
- ⅛ teaspoon salt
- 4 eggs, lightly beaten
- 2 tablespoons chopped fresh parsley
- ½ cup shredded reduced-fat Cheddar cheese
- 4 whole wheat tortillas (8" diameter)

HEAT 1 teaspoon of the oil in a large nonstick skillet over medium-high heat. Add the tomatoes and cook for 2 to 3 minutes, or until the tomatoes soften. Transfer to a plate, sprinkle with the salt, and set aside.

ADD the remaining 1 teaspoon oil to the skillet and reduce the heat to medium-low. Add the eggs and cook gently, using a spatula to gently push the eggs to the middle of the skillet as they set.

REMOVE the skillet from the heat and scatter the parsley and cheese over the eggs.

WARM the tortillas in the microwave oven on high power for 20 to 30 seconds. Place one-quarter of the egg mixture in the center of each tortilla and top with one-quarter of the tomatoes. Fold in the sides of each tortilla and roll into a cylinder, burrito-style.

TOTAL TIME: 15 minutes **MAKES 4**

PER WRAP: 243 calories, 14 g protein, 22 g carbohydrates, 11 g total fat, 3 g saturated fat, 4 g fiber, 402 mg sodium

Sun-Dried Tomato Wraps May Be a Veggie Impostor

The tomatoes provide little more than coloring. And watch out for sodium levels, which can soar. "If you want vegetables, stuff your wrap with them, but don't expect to get them in the wrap itself," says Karen Ansel, RD.

Spinach and Mushroom Breakfast Wraps

So how can this breakfast wrap make your morning brighter? Spinach contains lots of lutein, the sunshine-yellow pigment found in dark green leafy vegetables and egg yolks. Lutein has a "golden" reputation for guarding against age-related macular degeneration, a leading cause of blindness.

2 teaspoons olive oil

1 cup sliced mushrooms

1½ cups liquid egg substitute

2 eggs, beaten

½ cup crumbled reduced-fat feta cheese

4 cups fresh baby spinach

4 flour tortillas (10" diameter)

HEAT the oil in a large nonstick skillet over medium heat. Add the mushrooms and cook for 3 to 4 minutes, or until softened.

POUR the egg substitute, eggs, and cheese over the mushrooms and cook gently, using a spatula to gently push the egg substitute and eggs to the middle of the skillet as they set.

AFTER 2 minutes, add the spinach. Cook for 1 minute longer, or until the egg substitute and eggs are set and the spinach wilts.

WARM the tortillas in the microwave oven on high power for 20 to 30 seconds. Place one-quarter of the egg mixture in the center of each tortilla. Fold in the sides of each tortilla and roll into a cylinder, burrito-style.

TOTAL TIME: 10 minutes **MAKES 4**

PER WRAP: 402 calories, 25 g protein, 41 g carbohydrates, 16 g total fat, 4.5 g saturated fat, 4 g fiber, 922 mg sodium

Basic Breakfast Burrito

If you don't have time to separate eggs in the morning, keep a container of liquid egg whites on hand for recipes like this. A half cup is equal to four egg whites.

- ¼ cup diced lean ham
- 1 egg + 4 egg whites, beaten together
- 2 tablespoons chopped fresh cilantro
- ¼ cup shredded reduced-fat Cheddar cheese
- 1 whole wheat low-fat tortilla (10" diameter)
- 1 tablespoon salsa

HEAT a nonstick skillet coated with cooking spray over medium-high heat.

COOK the ham just until the surface starts to brown. Reduce the heat to medium-low.

POUR the eggs over the ham and cook gently, using a spatula to gently push the eggs to the middle of the skillet as they set. Sprinkle with the cilantro and cheese. Cook for 1 minute longer, or until the eggs are set and the cheese melts.

WARM the tortilla in the microwave oven on high power for 20 to 30 seconds. Place the egg mixture in the center of the tortilla and top with the salsa. Fold in the sides of the tortilla and roll into a cylinder, burrito-style.

TOTAL TIME: 15 minutes **MAKES 1 SERVING**

PER SERVING: 343 calories, 43 g protein, 14 g carbohydrates, 13 g total fat, 4 g saturated fat, 3 g fiber, 765 mg sodium

Western Egg Sandwich

This hearty breakfast sandwich packs a protein punch that will get you through the morning feeling strong. If sodium is a concern, use reduced-sodium ham instead.

1 whole wheat English muffin, split

1 egg

1 slice (1 ounce) deli ham

1 slice reduced-fat American cheese

1 teaspoon ketchup (optional)

TOAST the English muffin.

MEANWHILE, heat a small nonstick skillet coated with cooking spray over medium heat. Add the egg and cook, without stirring, for 1 minute, or until the egg white is set. Turn and cook for 1 minute longer.

WARM the ham by placing it next to the egg in the skillet during the last 30 seconds of the cooking time.

ASSEMBLE the sandwich by placing the ham, egg, and cheese on the bottom half of the toasted muffin. Top with the ketchup, if desired, and the remaining muffin half.

TOTAL TIME: 10 minutes **MAKES 1 SERVING**

PER SERVING: 256 calories, 20 g protein, 28 g carbohydrates, 8 g total fat, 3 g saturated fat, 4 g fiber, 852 mg sodium

Sausage and Apple Strata

Prepare this make-ahead casserole the night before for an effortless breakfast, or double the recipe for a Sunday brunch gathering. If you have leftovers, they warm up nicely in the microwave oven. Serve with a crisp green salad for a weekend lunch.

2 apples, peeled, cored, and coarsely chopped

¾ pound turkey breakfast sausage

2 whole wheat English muffins, cut into ½" pieces

3 scallions, chopped

¼ cup + 2 tablespoons shredded reduced-fat Swiss cheese

2 cups fat-free milk

8 egg whites

2 tablespoons grated Parmesan cheese

½ teaspoon mustard powder

¼ teaspoon ground black pepper

COAT a 2-quart (9" × 9") baking dish with cooking spray. Place the apples in a microwaveable bowl and cover. Microwave on high power for 3 minutes; uncover to cool.

HEAT a nonstick skillet coated with cooking spray over medium-low heat. Crumble the sausage and cook for 2 to 3 minutes, or until golden brown and cooked through. Scatter the apples, sausage, muffins, scallions, and Swiss in the bottom of the baking dish.

WHISK together the milk, egg whites, Parmesan, mustard, and pepper in a large bowl. Pour evenly over the sausage mixture in the dish. Cover with plastic wrap and refrigerate for 1 to 12 hours.

PREHEAT the oven to 375°F. Bake, uncovered, for 50 to 55 minutes, or until a knife inserted in the center comes out clean. Let stand for 15 minutes and serve hot or warm.

TOTAL TIME: 2 hours 25 minutes **MAKES 4 SERVINGS**

PER SERVING: 363 calories, 35 g protein, 33 g carbohydrates, 11 g total fat, 4 g saturated fat, 4 g fiber, 906 mg sodium

Colorful Turkey Bacon Strata

Studded with onion and bell peppers, this baked breakfast dish is pretty as well as delicious.

1 small red onion, chopped

½ green bell pepper, seeded and chopped

½ red bell pepper, seeded and chopped

2 slices extra-lean turkey bacon, chopped (cut crosswise into ¼"-wide strips)

4 slices multigrain bread, cut into ½" cubes

⅓ cup shredded reduced-fat Cheddar cheese

2 eggs

2 egg whites

1¾ cups fat-free milk

1 tablespoon Dijon mustard

¼ teaspoon ground black pepper

HEAT a 10" nonstick skillet coated with cooking spray over medium heat. Add the onion and bell peppers. Cook, stirring occasionally, for 8 minutes, or until the vegetables are almost tender. Stir in the bacon and cook for 2 minutes. Remove from the heat and stir in the bread cubes.

COAT an 11" × 7" baking dish with cooking spray and set on a baking sheet. Spoon the vegetable mixture into the baking dish. Sprinkle the cheese over the top.

WHISK together the eggs, egg whites, milk, mustard, and black pepper in a medium bowl. Pour evenly over the vegetable mixture in the baking dish. Let stand for at least 20 minutes, or cover and refrigerate for up to 12 hours.

PREHEAT the oven to 375°F. Bake the strata, uncovered, for 35 minutes, or until a knife inserted in the center comes out clean. Let stand for 10 minutes and serve hot.

TOTAL TIME: 1 hour 30 minutes **MAKES 4 SERVINGS**

PER SERVING: 218 calories, 16 g protein, 24 g carbohydrates, 6 g total fat, 2 g saturated fat, 5 g fiber, 482 mg sodium

Weekend Skillet Breakfast

This skillet dish is relatively easy to put together—so easy, in fact, that you might enjoy it as a luxurious start to your weekday.

4 small red potatoes, chopped

¼ cup water

2 teaspoons olive oil

¼ teaspoon salt

3 eggs, lightly beaten

1 scallion, chopped

1 tablespoon chopped fresh parsley

⅓ cup shredded reduced-fat smoked provolone cheese

COMBINE the potatoes, water, oil, and salt in a small nonstick skillet over medium-high heat. Cover and bring to a boil.

COOK until the water evaporates and the potatoes start to brown. Uncover and gently loosen the potatoes with a silicone or wooden spatula. Cook for 2 to 3 minutes or until crisp along the edges. Reduce the heat to low.

POUR the eggs over the potatoes and cook until the eggs begin to set. Sprinkle the scallion, parsley, and cheese over the top. Let stand until the cheese melts.

TOTAL TIME: 20 minutes **MAKES 2 SERVINGS**

PER SERVING: 455 calories, 21 g protein, 56 g carbohydrates, 18 g total fat, 6 g saturated fat, 6 g fiber, 586 mg sodium

Savory Salmon Brunch Skillet

Here's a great way to use leftover salmon, or feel free to substitute canned salmon if that's what you have on hand. Garnish your plate with extra dill, if you like.

⅔ cup fat-free sour cream

1 teaspoon lemon juice

2½ teaspoons chopped fresh dill, divided

¼ teaspoon salt

⅛ teaspoon ground black pepper

1 tablespoon olive oil

1 package (28 ounces) frozen diced potatoes with onions and peppers

2 cups flaked cooked salmon

2 scallions, chopped

1 teaspoon Dijon mustard

COMBINE the sour cream, lemon juice, and 1½ teaspoons of the dill in a small bowl. Season with the salt and pepper. Set aside.

HEAT the oil in a large nonstick skillet over medium heat. Add the potatoes and spread evenly over the bottom of the skillet. Cook, covered, stirring occasionally, for 10 minutes, or until heated through. Uncover, increase the heat to medium-high, and press potatoes with a large spatula. Cook, turning occasionally, for 5 minutes, or until browned and beginning to crisp.

MEANWHILE, combine the salmon, scallions, mustard, and remaining 1 teaspoon dill in a medium bowl.

ADD the salmon mixture to the skillet, combining with the potatoes by turning sections with the spatula (try not to break up the potatoes). Cook for 2 minutes, or until heated through. Serve with the dill cream.

TOTAL TIME: 20 minutes **MAKES 4 SERVINGS**

PER SERVING: 487 calories, 9 g protein, 91 g carbohydrates, 7 g total fat, 1 g saturated fat, 5 g fiber, 147 mg sodium

Sweet Potato Pancakes

These savory pancakes are typically made with white potatoes, but they get a fiber boost when made with sweet potatoes instead.

1 large sweet potato, peeled and cubed

2 scallions, chopped

2 egg whites

⅛ teaspoon ground black pepper

Pinch of grated nutmeg

2 teaspoons canola oil, divided

1 cup unsweetened applesauce

2 tablespoons reduced-fat sour cream

PLACE a steamer basket in a large pot with 1" of water. Bring to a boil over high heat. Steam the potato in the basket for 12 to 15 minutes, or until very tender. Place the potato in a large bowl and mash until almost smooth. Add the scallions, egg whites, pepper, and nutmeg and mash to combine.

HEAT 1 teaspoon of the oil in a nonstick skillet coated with cooking spray over medium heat. Drop half of the potato mixture by ¼ cupfuls into the skillet. Flatten into 3" rounds. Cook for 6 to 8 minutes, turning once, or until golden brown. Transfer to a plate and cover to keep warm.

REPEAT with the remaining 1 teaspoon oil and potato mixture to make 6 pancakes total. Serve the pancakes with the applesauce and sour cream.

TOTAL TIME: 35 minutes **MAKES 6**

PER SERVING (3 PANCAKES): 191 calories, 6 g protein, 29 g carbohydrates, 7 g total fat, 1 g saturated fat, 4 g fiber, 109 mg sodium

Pancakes with Blueberry Syrup

If blueberries are out of season, simply use frozen berries instead of fresh.

- ½ cup all-purpose flour
- ½ cup whole wheat pastry flour
- 2 tablespoons yellow cornmeal
- 2 tablespoons sugar
- 1 teaspoon baking powder
- ¼ teaspoon baking soda
- ⅛ teaspoon salt
- 1 cup buttermilk
- ¼ cup water
- 1 egg
- 1 tablespoon canola oil
- 1 tablespoon vanilla extract
- 2 cups blueberries
- ¼ cup honey

COMBINE the flours, cornmeal, sugar, baking powder, baking soda, and salt in a large bowl and mix well.

WHISK together the buttermilk, water, egg, oil, and vanilla in a medium bowl. Add to the flour mixture and whisk until smooth. Set aside.

COMBINE the blueberries and honey in a small saucepan. Cook over medium heat, stirring occasionally, for 5 minutes, or until the blueberries burst. Remove from the heat. The sauce will thicken slightly as it cools.

HEAT a large nonstick skillet coated with cooking spray over medium heat. Add the pancake batter by scant ¼ cupfuls and cook, in batches, for 2 minutes, or until the pancakes have puffed and the undersides are lightly browned. Turn the pancakes and cook for 2 minutes longer, or until lightly browned. Serve with the blueberry syrup.

TOTAL TIME: 35 minutes **MAKES 12**

PER SERVING (3 PANCAKES): 344 calories, 8 g protein, 65 g carbohydrates, 6 g total fat, 1 g saturated fat, 4 g fiber, 358 mg sodium

Baked Pancake with Berries and Cinnamon

Use any fruit spread you like for this recipe. You could also arrange 1 thinly sliced banana over the fruit spread before folding the pancake. Top each serving with a dollop of unsweetened whipped cream, and sprinkle with cinnamon or nutmeg, if desired.

4 eggs

½ cup 1% milk

⅓ cup oat flour

Pinch of salt

3 tablespoons unsalted butter, softened and divided

¼ teaspoon ground cinnamon

3 tablespoons raspberry or blueberry fruit spread, warmed

COMBINE the eggs, milk, flour, and salt in a blender. Process for 15 seconds, or until smooth. Pour into a medium bowl, cover, and let rest for 45 to 60 minutes at room temperature.

PREHEAT the oven to 375°F.

HEAT 2 tablespoons of the butter in a 9" ovenproof skillet over medium heat until frothy. Pour in the batter. Bake for 14 to 16 minutes, or until puffy and set.

REMOVE from the oven and sprinkle with the cinnamon. Slather the fruit spread over the pancake, and dot with the remaining 1 tablespoon butter. Fold the pancake in half (or use a spatula to roll it up) and slide it onto a platter. Slice the pancake into 4 pieces.

TOTAL TIME: 1 hour 30 minutes **MAKES 4 SERVINGS**

PER SERVING: 223 calories, 8 g protein, 15 g carbohydrates, 15 g total fat, 8 g saturated fat, 1 g fiber, 120 mg sodium

Bananas Foster French Toast

This recipe uses real butter and brown sugar, but just enough to get that sweet sensation without the postmeal crash.

- ¼ cup chopped pecans
- 2 tablespoons unsalted butter
- ¼ cup firmly packed brown sugar
- 2 tablespoons water
- 2 large bananas, peeled and cut into ½" rounds
- 1½ cups liquid egg substitute
- 1½ cups 1% milk
- 1 teaspoon vanilla extract
- 1 tablespoon ground cinnamon
- 8 slices (½" thick) challah or Italian bread

TOAST the pecans in a dry skillet over medium-high heat, tossing frequently, until fragrant. Place on a plate and set aside.

MELT the butter in a large nonstick skillet over medium heat. Add the brown sugar and water and stir until the sugar dissolves. Cook for 2 minutes, or until the mixture is frothy. Add the bananas and cook for 1 minute, or until tender. Transfer to a small bowl and keep warm.

HEAT a nonstick griddle coated with cooking spray over medium heat. In a large baking dish, whisk together the egg substitute, milk, vanilla, and cinnamon. Dip the bread in the batter and thoroughly coat both sides. Place on the hot griddle and cook for 2 minutes per side, or until golden brown.

SERVE each slice topped with equal amounts of the banana mixture and toasted pecans.

TOTAL TIME: 30 minutes **MAKES 8 SERVINGS**

PER SERVING: 208 calories, 9 g protein, 29 g carbohydrates, 6 g total fat, 3 g saturated fat, 2 g fiber, 234 mg sodium

Decadent Raspberry French Toast

Why is 0% Greek yogurt such a perfect breakfast food? It has zero cholesterol and 14 grams of protein per cup, which helps keep you feeling full. It also contains calcium and potassium, which help regulate blood pressure.

1 cup raspberries, divided

¾ cup 0% vanilla Greek yogurt, divided

1 teaspoon honey

2 teaspoons butter

1 egg

2 slices whole wheat bread

2 tablespoons chopped pecans

COMBINE ½ cup of the raspberries, ¼ cup of the yogurt, and the honey in a small bowl. Mash with the back of a fork until smooth. Set aside.

MELT the butter in a nonstick skillet over medium heat.

MIX the egg and remaining ½ cup yogurt in a shallow bowl. Dip both sides of the bread in the egg mixture, removing excess so that only a thin layer remains on the outside of the bread. Place the bread in the skillet and cook for 2 minutes per side, or until lightly browned.

SERVE the toast topped with the raspberry-yogurt mixture, the remaining ½ cup raspberries, and pecans.

TOTAL TIME: 20 minutes **MAKES 1 SERVING**

PER SERVING: 563 calories, 32 g protein, 61 g carbohydrates, 24 g total fat, 8 g saturated fat, 5 g fiber, 454 mg sodium

Sandwiches

CHAPTER

6

Veggie Sandwiches with Edamame Hummus

Served with a knife and fork, this filling sandwich will satisfy your lunchtime cravings. Wrap each half separately if you're taking this sandwich on the go.

¾ **cup frozen shelled edamame**

⅓ **cup 0% plain Greek yogurt**

3 **tablespoons chopped fresh parsley**

2 **tablespoons chopped fresh chives**

1 **tablespoon lemon juice**

1 **teaspoon honey mustard**
Generous pinch of salt

4 **thin slices whole wheat bread, toasted**

¾ **cup fresh baby spinach**

1 **tomato, sliced**

1 **Kirby cucumber, sliced**

BRING a small saucepan of water to a boil. Add the edamame and cook for 5 minutes, or until tender. Drain well. Place in a mini food processor and process until finely chopped. Add the yogurt, parsley, chives, lemon juice, mustard, and salt. Process until smooth.

SPREAD 2 tablespoons of the edamame hummus on each slice of the bread. Top with the spinach. Spoon ½ tablespoon of the hummus on top of each sandwich. Top with the tomato, cucumber, and a final dollop of hummus. Serve 2 open-face sandwiches per person.

TOTAL TIME: 20 minutes **MAKES 4**

PER SERVING (2 SANDWICHES): 224 calories, 15 g protein, 36 g carbohydrates, 4 g total fat, 0 g saturated fat, 11 g fiber, 380 mg sodium

Caribbean Tofu and Veggie Sandwiches

Smoked tofu is much more dense and flavorful than water-packed tofu. Available in a variety of flavors, it's great in sandwiches or salads.

1 onion, quartered

1 red bell pepper, seeded and quartered

¼ cup 0% plain Greek yogurt

1 teaspoon grated orange peel

1 teaspoon honey

2 cups mesclun or baby romaine

1 package (8 ounces) Caribbean-flavored smoked tofu, cut into 12 slices

8 slices light, high-fiber, whole wheat bread

PREHEAT the oven to 400°F. Place the onion and pepper on a baking sheet coated with cooking spray and coat the tops of the vegetables with cooking spray. Roast for 15 minutes, turning once, or until tender and browned.

MEANWHILE, stir together the yogurt, orange peel, and honey in a small bowl.

LAYER the mesclun or baby romaine, roasted vegetables, and tofu on each of 4 bread slices. Top with the yogurt spread and remaining bread slices.

TOTAL TIME: 35 minutes   **MAKES 4**

PER SANDWICH: 214 calories, 15 g protein, 31 g carbohydrates, 6 g total fat, 1 g saturated fat, 8 g fiber, 258 mg sodium

Seven-Grain Veggie-Delight Sandwich

You'll be hard pressed to miss lunchmeat in a veggie-loaded sandwich like this.

2 teaspoons stone-ground mustard

2 slices seven-grain sandwich bread, toasted

1 slice (1 ounce) sharp Cheddar cheese

¼ cup thinly sliced cucumber

1 small carrot, shredded

¼ cup alfalfa sprouts

SPREAD the mustard on each slice of the bread. Layer the cheese, cucumber, carrot, and sprouts on 1 slice of the bread. Top with the remaining bread slice.

TOTAL TIME: 5 minutes **MAKES 1 SERVING**

PER SERVING: 368 calories, 15 g protein, 46 g carbohydrates, 13 g total fat, 7 g saturated fat, 6 g fiber, 728 mg sodium

Pizza May Be a Veggie Impostor

No joke: In 2011, Congress ruled that pizza counts as a veggie in school lunches, since a slice has about 2 tablespoons of tomato paste. But with all that crust and cheese (refined carbs and saturated fats), most pizza is not ideal.

Egg Salad

Excellent served with crackers or on toasted white bread, this classic recipe is a quick and easy means to a healthy lunch.

6 **hard-cooked eggs, peeled**

¼ **cup reduced-fat mayonnaise**

2 **tablespoons spicy brown mustard**

¼ **cup finely chopped celery**

2 **tablespoons chopped red onion**

2 **tablespoons sweet pickle relish**

2 **tablespoons chopped fresh parsley**

SLICE the eggs in half and place the yolks in a medium bowl. Mash the yolks with the back of a fork and stir in the mayonnaise and mustard.

CHOP the egg whites and add to the bowl along with the celery, onion, relish, and parsley. Stir gently until thoroughly combined.

TOTAL TIME: 5 minutes **MAKES 4 SERVINGS**

PER SERVING: 185 calories, 10 g protein, 6 g carbohydrates, 13 g total fat, 3 g saturated fat, 0 g fiber, 337 mg sodium

Tuna and Water Chestnut Sandwiches

Not a big celery fan? Then this might be the tuna sandwich you've been waiting for. The water chestnuts add a nice crunchy element to every bite without the flavor of celery.

1 can (6 ounces) solid white tuna packed in water, drained

⅔ cup coarsely chopped canned water chestnuts, drained

2 tablespoons mayonnaise

2 tablespoons pickle relish

4 slices whole wheat bread

2 leaves lettuce

FLAKE the tuna with a fork into a bowl. Add the water chestnuts, mayonnaise, and relish. Stir to combine.

SPREAD the tuna mixture on 2 slices of the bread. Top with the lettuce and remaining bread slices.

TOTAL TIME: 5 minutes **MAKES 2**

PER SANDWICH: 327 calories, 24 g protein, 38 g carbohydrates, 9 g total fat, 2 g saturated fat, 6 g fiber, 794 mg sodium

Curried Chicken Salad Sandwiches with Raisins

A quick soak in hot water helps the raisins plump up so that they lend even more texture and flavor to this sweet and spicy sandwich.

3 tablespoons golden raisins

3 cups chopped cooked chicken breast

2 ribs celery, finely chopped

½ onion, finely chopped

1 carrot, shredded

½ teaspoon curry powder

¼ cup light mayonnaise

¼ teaspoon salt

⅛ teaspoon ground black pepper

4 large leaves lettuce

8 slices whole grain bread or English muffin halves, toasted

2 tomatoes, sliced

SOAK the raisins in enough hot water to cover in a small bowl for at least 10 minutes. Drain and place in a large bowl. Add the chicken, celery, onion, carrot, curry powder, mayonnaise, salt, and pepper. Mix well.

PLACE a lettuce leaf on each of 4 bread slices or muffin halves and top with the tomatoes, chicken salad, and remaining bread slices or muffin halves.

TOTAL TIME: 25 minutes **MAKES 4**

PER SANDWICH: 437 calories, 40 g protein, 42 g carbohydrates, 12 g total fat, 2 g saturated fat, 11 g fiber, 556 mg sodium

Turkey, Apple, and Chutney Sandwiches

The creamy chutney spread takes this sandwich from ordinary to exciting. If you don't have chutney on hand, substitute 1 tablespoon apricot jam and a pinch of curry powder.

1 tablespoon chutney, large chunks finely chopped (if necessary)

1 tablespoon reduced-fat sour cream

1 teaspoon lemon juice

4 thin slices 100% whole wheat bread

½ cup fresh baby spinach

3 ounces sliced low-sodium turkey breast

2 thin slices (1 ounce total) reduced-fat Swiss cheese

1 small Granny Smith apple, thinly sliced

STIR together the chutney, sour cream, and lemon juice in a small bowl.

SPREAD the chutney mixture on 2 slices of the bread. Top with the spinach, turkey, cheese, apple, and remaining bread slices. Cut in half to serve.

TOTAL TIME: 15 minutes **MAKES 2**

PER SANDWICH: 250 calories, 21 g protein, 30 g carbohydrates, 6 g total fat, 3 g saturated fat, 7 g fiber, 331 mg sodium

Quick Turkey-Veggie Wrap

The sunflower seeds in this recipe provide about 20 percent of the Recommended Dietary Allowance (RDA) of vitamin E, an important antioxidant for preventing sun damage.

1 **whole wheat tortilla (8" diameter)**

1 **tablespoon low-fat cream cheese**

½ **cup fresh baby spinach**

4 **ounces sliced turkey breast**

2 **tablespoons shredded carrot**

1 **tablespoon sunflower seeds**

SPREAD the tortilla with the cream cheese and layer with the spinach, turkey, carrot, and sunflower seeds. Fold in the sides of the tortilla and roll into a cylinder, burrito-style. Cut in half on a diagonal to serve.

TOTAL TIME: 5 minutes **MAKES 1**

PER WRAP: 324 calories, 41 g protein, 25 g carbohydrates, 4 g total fat, 2.5 g saturated fat, 4 g fiber, 304 mg sodium

WHY YOU SHOULD CHOOSE

Carrots

Don't skip the carrots in this wrap sandwich—they provide a nice, sweet crunch to the finished dish.

Niçoise Salad Wraps

Tuna is a very healthy fish to include in your diet. A 3-ounce piece contains 1,300 milligrams of omega-3s and a respectable amount of vitamin D to boot.

¾ **pound yellowfin tuna steaks**

1 **pound green beans**

1 **tablespoon lemon juice**

1½ **teaspoons white wine vinegar**

½ **teaspoon Dijon mustard**

3 **tablespoons olive oil**

1 **teaspoon dried tarragon**

½ **teaspoon salt**

½ **teaspoon ground black pepper**

4 **cups salad greens**

4 **multigrain sandwich wraps (10" diameter)**

16 **cherry tomatoes, halved**

2 **hard-cooked eggs, peeled and sliced**

16 **pitted kalamata olives**

PREHEAT the grill or broiler. Grill or broil the tuna 6" from the heat for 3 minutes per side, or until just slightly pink in the center. Allow to cool and then flake.

PLACE a steamer basket in a large pot with 2" of water. Bring to a boil over high heat. Steam the green beans in the basket for 5 to 8 minutes, or until tender-crisp. Cut into 1" pieces.

COMBINE the lemon juice, vinegar, and mustard in a small bowl. Slowly whisk in the oil until emulsified. Season with the tarragon, salt, and pepper.

PLACE the salad greens across the lower half of each wrap. Top with the green beans, tomatoes, eggs, olives, and flaked tuna. Drizzle each wrap with 1 tablespoon of the dressing. Fold in the sides of each wrap and roll into a cylinder, burrito-style. Cut in half on a diagonal to serve.

TOTAL TIME: 20 minutes **MAKES 4**

PER WRAP: 369 calories, 30 g protein, 34 g carbohydrates, 16 g total fat, 3 g saturated fat, 3 g fiber, 566 mg sodium

Meatless Gyros

This Greek-inspired sandwich includes a hearty, garlicky filling slathered with a creamy cucumber sauce. You'll never miss the meat!

¼ **pound red new potatoes**

5 **cloves garlic, minced and divided**

1 **cucumber, peeled and grated**

1 **cup 0% plain Greek yogurt**

¼ **teaspoon salt**

⅛ **teaspoon ground black pepper**

2 **teaspoons olive oil**

½ **cup crumbled feta cheese**

2 **tablespoons finely chopped red onion**

4 **whole wheat pitas (6–7" diameter)**

2 **cups shredded romaine lettuce**

2 **plum tomatoes, chopped**

COVER the potatoes with water in a large saucepan. Cover and bring to a boil over medium-high heat. Reduce the heat to a simmer and cook for 15 minutes, or until the potatoes are tender.

MEANWHILE, measure 1 teaspoon of the minced garlic and set in a small bowl. Squeeze the cucumber to extract and discard as much juice as possible. Add the cucumber, yogurt, salt, and pepper to the bowl and stir to combine. Set aside.

COMBINE the oil and remaining 4 cloves garlic in a small microwaveable bowl. Microwave on high power for 1 minute at 50 percent power.

DRAIN the potatoes, reserving ½ cup of the cooking liquid. Return the potatoes to the saucepan, add the garlic-oil mixture, and mash to combine. Add the cheese and onion and continue mashing until thick and lumpy, adding the reserved cooking liquid a spoonful at a time, if necessary, to reach the desired consistency.

WARM the pitas in a skillet over medium-high heat for 1 minute.

SPREAD equal portions of the potato mixture and yogurt sauce on each pita. Top with the lettuce and tomatoes before serving.

TOTAL TIME: 25 minutes **MAKES 4**

PER GYRO: 316 calories, 16 g protein, 48 g carbohydrates, 8 g total fat, 3 g saturated fat, 7 g fiber, 650 mg sodium

Greek Salad Wrap

Tapenade is a thick paste made from capers, anchovies, ripe olives, olive oil, lemon juice, and other seasonings. Look for it near the pickled condiments or in the olive bar section of your grocery store.

- **2** tablespoons 0% plain Greek yogurt
- **1** tablespoon tapenade
- **1½** teaspoons orange juice
- **¼** teaspoon grated orange peel
- **1½** cups loosely packed fresh baby spinach
- **¼** cup grape tomatoes, halved
- **¼** small cucumber, peeled, halved, seeded, and sliced
- **1** whole wheat tortilla (10" diameter)
- **1** tablespoon crumbled feta cheese

WHISK together the yogurt, tapenade, orange juice, and orange peel in a large bowl. Add the spinach, tomatoes, and cucumber and toss to coat well.

WARM the tortilla in the microwave oven on high power for 20 to 30 seconds. Arrange the spinach mixture on top and sprinkle with the cheese.

FOLD in the sides of the tortilla and roll into a cylinder, burrito-style. Cut in half on a diagonal to serve.

TOTAL TIME: 10 minutes   **MAKES 1**

PER WRAP: 230 calories, 8 g protein, 29 g carbohydrates, 10 g total fat, 2 g saturated fat, 7 g fiber, 679 mg sodium

Healthy Souvlaki Sandwiches

The word *souvlaki* comes from the Greek word *souvla*, which means "skewer." If you choose to use bamboo skewers instead of metal skewers, make sure to soak them in water for a half hour beforehand so they don't burn.

1 pound boneless, skinless chicken breasts, cut into 20 cubes

2 tablespoons red wine vinegar, divided

1 teaspoon dried oregano

5 teaspoons olive oil, divided

3 cloves garlic, minced and divided

2 cups shredded romaine lettuce

2 plum tomatoes, chopped

½ cucumber, peeled, seeded, and thinly sliced

½ small white onion, finely chopped

½ teaspoon salt, divided

¼ teaspoon ground black pepper, divided

1 container (6 ounces) 0% plain Greek yogurt

4 whole grain pitas (6½" diameter), top one-fourth sliced off

COMBINE the chicken, 1 tablespoon of the vinegar, oregano, 2 teaspoons of the oil, and 2 cloves of the garlic in a medium bowl. Let stand for 20 minutes, tossing occasionally.

MEANWHILE, combine the lettuce, tomatoes, cucumber, onion, ¼ teaspoon of the salt, ⅛ teaspoon of the pepper, and the remaining 1 tablespoon vinegar and 3 teaspoons oil in a separate medium bowl. Combine the yogurt and remaining 1 clove garlic in a large bowl.

PREHEAT the broiler. Coat a broiler-pan rack with cooking spray.

THREAD 5 chicken cubes onto each of 4 metal skewers. Sprinkle with the remaining ¼ teaspoon salt and ⅛ teaspoon pepper. Place on the broiler pan and broil 4" to 5" from the heat for 8 to 10 minutes, turning often. Let cool slightly. Remove the chicken from the skewers and combine with the yogurt mixture in the bowl.

FILL each pita with equal portions of the lettuce mixture and chicken mixture.

TOTAL TIME: 50 minutes **MAKES 4**

PER SANDWICH: 386 calories, 33 g protein, 43 g carbohydrates, 10 g total fat, 2 g saturated fat, 6 g fiber, 723 mg sodium

Turkey Sandwiches with Edamame Relish

A popular snack food in Japan, edamame are green soybeans, available in the freezer or produce section of most supermarkets. In this sandwich, they add a bit more texture as a light relish to an otherwise simple combination.

1 tomato

¼ cup shelled edamame (thawed, if frozen)

½ teaspoon olive oil

¼ teaspoon red wine vinegar

¼ avocado, peeled and pitted

1 whole wheat mini pita (4" diameter), split

2 ounces sliced turkey breast

1 leaf romaine lettuce, chopped

CUT 2 slices from the tomato and set aside. Chop the remaining tomato. Place the chopped tomato, edamame, oil, and vinegar in a small bowl and toss to coat.

MASH the avocado with the back of a fork and spread on the rough side of each pita half. Top each pita half with the turkey, lettuce, reserved sliced tomato, and edamame mixture and fold in half, taco-style. Serve any remaining edamame mixture on the side.

TOTAL TIME: 15 minutes **MAKES 1**

PER SANDWICH: 327 calories, 26 g protein, 30 g carbohydrates, 13 g total fat, 2 g saturated fat, 9 g fiber, 203 mg sodium

Grown-Up Grilled Cheese

//

Most people list grilled cheese among their favorite comfort foods, so this is hardly a dish that should drop from the menu when weight loss is the goal. Here, whole wheat bread provides an extra fiber boost, and a generous amount of mozzarella gets a little flavor kick from the fresh tomato.

1 teaspoon olive oil

2 slices (or ½ cup shredded) part-skim mozzarella cheese

2 slices tomato

2 slices whole wheat bread

Dried oregano

HEAT the oil in a nonstick skillet over medium heat.

LAYER the cheese and tomato on 1 slice of the bread. Sprinkle with the oregano to taste. Cover with the remaining bread slice.

GRILL the sandwich in the skillet for 3 minutes per side, or until the cheese melts.

//

TOTAL TIME: 7 minutes **MAKES 1**

PER SANDWICH: 343 calories, 23 g protein, 27 g carbohydrates, 16 g total fat, 7 g saturated fat, 4 g fiber, 275 mg sodium

Grilled Vegetable and Mozzarella Sandwiches

While you may be tempted to save time using the grilled vegetables in your grocery's deli case, try to make your own if possible. The best way to control the amount of fat and calories in any finished dish is to rely on your own ingredients whenever you can.

3 tablespoons water

1 tablespoon cider vinegar

2 teaspoons olive oil

1 teaspoon light brown sugar

1 summer squash, cut lengthwise into ¼"-thick slices

1 large red onion, thickly sliced

1 red bell pepper, seeded and cut lengthwise into flat panels

1 loaf whole grain Italian bread (8 ounces), halved lengthwise

½ cup barbecue sauce

4 ounces part-skim mozzarella cheese, thinly sliced

COAT a grill rack with cooking spray. Preheat the grill to medium heat.

WHISK together the water, vinegar, oil, and sugar in a large bowl. Add the squash and onion and toss gently to coat.

PLACE the pepper, skin side down, on the grill rack. Add the squash and onion. Grill the squash and onion for 10 minutes, turning occasionally, or until tender-crisp. Grill the pepper for 10 minutes, without turning, or until the skin is charred. Transfer the vegetables to a plate. When cool enough to handle, peel the pepper and cut into thick strips.

GRILL the bread, cut sides down, for 30 seconds, or until lightly toasted. Brush the toasted surfaces of the bread with the barbecue sauce.

TOP the bottom half of the bread with the cheese and vegetables. Cover with the top half of the bread and return to the grill. Cover and grill for 30 seconds, or until the cheese melts. Cut crosswise into 4 sandwiches.

TOTAL TIME: 25 minutes **MAKES 4**

PER SANDWICH: 294 calories, 12 g protein, 45 g carbohydrates, 9 g total fat, 4 g saturated fat, 10 g fiber, 680 mg sodium

Meatless Muffulettas

Known as one of the signature sandwiches in New Orleans, a muffuletta is traditionally stuffed with layers of capicola, salami, pepperoni, and ham—not exactly the type of foods we turn to when we want to lose weight. That's why this lightened-up version skips the meat while delivering plenty of great flavors.

16 pitted black olives, chopped

2 teaspoons balsamic vinegar

2 teaspoons olive oil

¼ teaspoon red-pepper flakes

4 Portuguese rolls, split

4 slices (4 ounces total) smoked provolone cheese

4 thin slices red onion

8 canned artichoke hearts, drained and chopped

¼ cup sliced roasted red bell pepper

COMBINE the olives, vinegar, oil, and red-pepper flakes in a small bowl.

PLACE a spoonful of the olive mixture on each of the roll bottoms. Top with the onion, artichokes, roasted pepper, and cheese. Top with the remaining olive mixture and cover with the roll tops, pressing down firmly to pack layers. Cut in half before serving.

TOTAL TIME: 15 minutes **MAKES 4**

PER MUFFULETTA: 284 calories, 12 g protein, 30 g carbohydrates, 14 g total fat, 5 g saturated fat, 3 g fiber, 861 mg sodium

Veggie Chips May Be a Veggie Impostor

Don't be misled by photos on the bag. Check to see if real veggies are near the top of the ingredients list. They probably aren't. And since they're dehydrated and not as filling as the real thing, you eat more calories.

Cuban Sandwiches

This Latin riff on a grilled ham and cheese sandwich traditionally features a Cuban bread base loaded up with ham, pork, Swiss cheese, pickles, and mustard. Here, we've skipped the ham but kept all the other key ingredients for a delicious pressed sandwich.

¾ **pound pork tenderloin, trimmed of all visible fat**

1 **teaspoon olive oil**

1 **clove garlic, minced**

¼ **teaspoon salt**

⅛ **teaspoon ground black pepper**

1 **loaf multigrain Italian bread (8 ounces), cut into 4 sections and then each halved lengthwise**

4 **teaspoons yellow mustard**

4 **thin slices (2 ounces total) reduced-fat Swiss cheese**

2 **small dill pickles, thinly sliced**

PREHEAT the oven to 425°F. Coat a wire rack with cooking spray and place on a shallow baking pan.

RUB the pork tenderloin with the oil and garlic. Sprinkle with the salt and pepper. Place on the wire rack and roast for 30 to 35 minutes, or until a thermometer inserted in the center registers 160°F and the juices run clear. Let the pork stand for 15 minutes before thinly slicing across the grain.

SPREAD the cut sides of the bottom bread pieces with the mustard. Top each with the cheese, pork, and an overlapping layer of pickles. Top with the remaining bread pieces.

HEAT a large nonstick skillet over medium heat. Add the sandwiches, top sides down, and place a heavy skillet on top of the sandwiches, pressing down slightly to flatten. Cook for 6 minutes. Turn the sandwiches over and replace the heavy skillet on top. Cook for 5 to 6 minutes, or until the cheese melts and the sandwiches are flat and heated through.

REMOVE from the skillet and cut each sandwich in half at a sharp angle. Serve immediately.

TOTAL TIME: 1 hour 10 minutes **MAKES 4**

PER SANDWICH: 273 calories, 24 g protein, 27 g carbohydrates, 6 g total fat, 2 g saturated fat, 2 g fiber, 899 mg sodium

Wild Mushroom–Lentil Burgers

These burgers pack an impressive amount of fiber into every serving—almost a half a day's worth!

6 ounces shiitake mushrooms

1 can (15.5 ounces) lentils, rinsed and drained

¾ cup soft whole wheat bread crumbs (from 1 slice)

1 egg

¼ cup chopped celery

1½ tablespoons chopped fresh thyme

2 teaspoons Dijon mustard

1 cup chopped onion, divided

4 ounces mild goat cheese, divided

6 tablespoons fine yellow cornmeal

3 teaspoons olive oil, divided

4 whole wheat buns, toasted

¼ cup chopped roasted red bell pepper

¼ cup watercress

PREHEAT the oven to 400°F.

REMOVE and discard the stems from the mushrooms. Coarsely chop three-fourths of the mushroom caps and put in a food processor. Quarter the remaining mushroom caps and set aside.

ADD the lentils, bread crumbs, egg, celery, thyme, mustard, ½ cup of the onion, and 2 ounces of the cheese to the food processor. Pulse until coarsely chopped. Form into 4 patties (3" diameter). Place the cornmeal on a plate and gently coat the patties on all sides (patties will be very delicate).

HEAT 1 teaspoon of the oil in a large nonstick skillet over medium heat. Add the reserved mushroom quarters and remaining ½ cup onion and cook for 5 to 6 minutes, or until the onion is golden brown. Remove from the skillet and set aside.

ADD the remaining 2 teaspoons oil to the skillet and cook the patties for 6 minutes, turning once, or until golden brown. Transfer to a baking sheet and top with the remaining 2 ounces cheese. Bake for 4 minutes, or until heated through.

SERVE the burgers on the buns and top with the mushroom mixture, pepper, and watercress.

TOTAL TIME: 30 minutes **MAKES 4**

PER BURGER: 386 calories, 19 g protein, 51 g carbohydrates, 13 g total fat, 5.5 g saturated fat, 12 g fiber, 574 mg sodium

Tropical Veggie Burgers

To test your avocado for ripeness, press it gently—the flesh should give just slightly. Avocados ripen at room temperature, and you can speed up the process by placing them in a closed paper bag for a day. Once ripe, they'll keep in the refrigerator for a few days.

2 plum tomatoes, chopped

1 mango, peeled, seeded, and chopped

½ avocado, peeled, pitted, and chopped

2 tablespoons finely chopped red onion

2 tablespoons finely chopped fresh cilantro

1 tablespoon lime juice

4 frozen veggie burgers

4 whole wheat mini pitas (4" diameter), split

½ cup shredded pepper Jack cheese

4 leaves romaine lettuce

COMBINE the tomatoes, mango, avocado, onion, cilantro, and lime juice in a large bowl. Let sit to allow the flavors to combine.

MEANWHILE, cook the burgers according to the package directions.

SERVE the burgers in the pitas with the cheese, lettuce, and mango mixture.

TOTAL TIME: 20 minutes **MAKES 4**

PER BURGER: 332 calories, 19 g protein, 38 g carbohydrates, 13 g total fat, 4 g saturated fat, 8 g fiber, 593 mg sodium

Grilled Chicken and Pineapple Sandwiches

When buying pineapple, keep in mind that size really doesn't matter. Instead, look for pineapples that are heavy for their size. While larger pineapples will have more edible flesh, there is usually no difference in quality.

4 boneless, skinless chicken breast halves (6 ounces each)

Teriyaki sauce

4 slices (4 ounces total) Swiss cheese

4 slices fresh pineapple (½" thick)

4 whole wheat sandwich rolls

½ red onion, thinly sliced

¼ cup pickled jalapeño chile pepper slices or 1 fresh jalapeño chile pepper, thinly sliced (wear plastic gloves when handling fresh chile peppers)

COMBINE the chicken and enough teriyaki sauce to cover it in a resealable plastic bag. Marinate in the refrigerator for at least 30 minutes or up to 12 hours.

COAT a grill rack with cooking spray. Preheat the grill to medium heat. Remove the chicken from the marinade, discarding any remaining marinade. Grill the chicken for 20 minutes, turning once, or until a thermometer inserted in the center of a breast registers 165°F and the juices run clear. Remove from the grill; top with the cheese and set aside.

MEANWHILE, place the pineapple and rolls on the grill. Grill the rolls for 1 minute, or until lightly toasted. Grill the pineapple for 2 minutes per side, or until soft and caramelized. Top the roll bottoms with the chicken, pineapple, onion, and jalapeño. If desired, drizzle with additional teriyaki sauce. Cover with roll tops.

TOTAL TIME: 1 hour **MAKES 4**

PER SANDWICH: 391 calories, 36 g protein, 34 g carbohydrates, 13 g total fat, 6 g saturated fat, 5 g fiber, 717 mg sodium

Cheesesteak Sandwiches

The original steak sandwich has distinct Philadelphia origins, but it has become popular throughout the country for good reason—it's satisfying and delicious. While this version is still loaded with grilled onions, a light blue cheese sauce makes a flavorful stand-in for the standard processed cheese spread.

2 tablespoons 0% plain Greek yogurt

2 tablespoons reduced-fat mayonnaise

¼ cup crumbled blue cheese

2 teaspoons olive oil

1 large onion, sliced

1 tablespoon sugar

1 pound flank steak

¼ teaspoon salt

⅛ teaspoon ground black pepper

2 cups arugula

2 tomatoes, sliced

4 whole wheat sandwich rolls

COMBINE the yogurt, mayonnaise, and blue cheese in a small bowl. Set aside.

HEAT the oil in a large nonstick skillet over medium-high heat. Add the onion and cook, turning frequently, for 5 minutes, or until soft. Sprinkle with the sugar, reduce the heat, and cook for 1 minute, or until the onion is browned and caramelized. Remove from the heat and set aside.

COAT a grill rack with cooking spray. Preheat the grill to medium heat. Season the steak with the salt and pepper and grill for 3 to 4 minutes per side (for medium-rare), or until the steak is firm but still gives with gentle pressure. Let stand for at least 5 minutes before slicing into thin strips.

DIVIDE the arugula and tomatoes among the roll bottoms. Top with the steak and caramelized onion. Drizzle each sandwich with the blue cheese sauce and cover with the roll tops.

TOTAL TIME: 30 minutes **MAKES 4**

PER SANDWICH: 544 calories, 36 g protein, 59 g carbohydrates, 20 g total fat, 7 g saturated fat, 9 g fiber, 776 mg sodium

Soups

Chilled Cucumber Soup with Shrimp

On a warm summer day, this soup is a cool pick-me-up. If you're not a seafood fan, simply omit the shrimp.

3 cups buttermilk, divided

¾ cup cooked shelled edamame, divided

2 small Kirby cucumbers, peeled, seeded, and coarsely chopped

1 tablespoon lime juice

1 teaspoon extra-virgin olive oil

2 tablespoons chopped fresh mint

3 tablespoons chopped fresh chives, divided

½ pound peeled and deveined cooked medium shrimp

8 rye crispbread crackers

Lime wedges

COMBINE 1 cup of the buttermilk and ½ cup of the edamame in a food processor or blender and process until smooth. Add the cucumbers, lime juice, oil, and the remaining 2 cups buttermilk. Process until smooth. Add the mint and 2 tablespoons of the chives. Process until the herbs are finely chopped. Divide the mixture among 4 bowls.

SET aside 4 shrimp for the garnish and coarsely chop the remaining shrimp. Divide the chopped shrimp and remaining ¼ cup edamame among the bowls. Garnish with the whole shrimp and remaining 1 tablespoon chives. Serve with the crackers and lime wedges.

TOTAL TIME: 25 minutes **MAKES 4 SERVINGS**

PER SERVING: 184 calories, 20 g protein, 14 g carbohydrates, 5 g total fat, 1.5 g saturated fat, 2 g fiber, 270 mg sodium

Minted Melon Soup

Chilled soups can be wonderfully refreshing and portable. This one is perfect for a summer picnic at the beach.

7 cups cubed honeydew melon or cantaloupe

¼ cup lemon or lime juice

8 fresh mint leaves

1 tablespoon honey

¼ teaspoon ground nutmeg

⅛ teaspoon almond extract

Pinch of salt

COMBINE the honeydew melon or cantaloupe, lemon or lime juice, mint, honey, nutmeg, almond extract, and salt in a food processor or blender and puree until smooth. Refrigerate for at least 1 hour or up to 2 days.

TOTAL TIME: 5 minutes + chilling time **MAKES 4 SERVINGS**

PER SERVING: 128 calories, 2 g protein, 33 g carbohydrates, 1 g total fat, 0 g saturated fat, 3 g fiber, 127 mg sodium

Spring Pea Soup

Place the peas in an ice water bath immediately after cooking to help keep this soup bright green and springtime fresh.

2 pounds fresh green peas, shelled, or 10 ounces frozen

2⅔ cups vegetable broth

2⅔ cups cold water

3 tablespoons sugar

⅛ teaspoon ground black pepper

COOK the peas in boiling water in a large saucepan for 10 minutes, or until soft. Drain and place the colander in a bowl of ice water. Drain again.

COMBINE the peas and broth in a food processor or blender and puree until thick and smooth.

TRANSFER the mixture to the saucepan and stir in the water, sugar, and pepper. Warm the soup over medium heat, if desired, or serve cold.

TOTAL TIME: 15 minutes **MAKES 4 SERVINGS**

PER SERVING: 229 calories, 12 g protein, 45 g carbohydrates, 1 g total fat, 0 g saturated fat, 12 g fiber, 275 mg sodium

Minestrone

There are probably as many recipes for minestrone as there are cooks who enjoy making it. This hearty version is chock-full of vegetables and perfect for Meatless Mondays.

1 tablespoon olive oil

1 large onion, chopped

1 large rib celery, chopped

1 large carrot, chopped

½ teaspoon salt, divided

2 cloves garlic, minced

1 teaspoon dried oregano

2 quarts low-sodium vegetable broth

1 can (14.5 ounces) diced tomatoes

1 cup ditalini (short tube) pasta

4 cups chopped escarole

1 cup frozen green peas

Freshly grated Parmesan cheese (optional)

HEAT the oil in a large saucepan over medium-high heat. Add the onion, celery, and carrot. Sprinkle with ¼ teaspoon of the salt. Cook, stirring occasionally, for 5 to 7 minutes, or until the vegetables begin to soften.

ADD the garlic and oregano. Cook for 1 to 2 minutes, or until fragrant. Add the broth, tomatoes, and pasta and bring to a boil.

REDUCE the heat and cover. Simmer for 15 minutes. Remove from the heat and add the remaining ¼ teaspoon salt. Just before serving, add the escarole and peas. Stir until the escarole wilts and the peas are tender. Serve sprinkled with the cheese, if desired.

TOTAL TIME: 40 minutes   **MAKES 8 SERVINGS**

PER SERVING: 124 calories, 4 g protein, 22 g carbohydrates, 2 g total fat, 0.5 g saturated fat, 4 g fiber, 437 mg sodium

Simply Slimming Vegetable Soup

Forget canned vegetable soup—some brands can pack close to a day's worth of sodium into one can. Instead, opt for homemade soups like this one that are quick to put together and make good use of extra veggies.

1 tablespoon olive oil

1 small carrot, chopped

1 rib celery, chopped

4 ounces mushrooms, chopped

2 cloves garlic, chopped

1 can (14.5 ounces) diced tomatoes

1 cup chicken broth

1 cup fresh spinach, chopped

¼ cup chopped fresh parsley

2 teaspoons lemon juice

¼ teaspoon salt

⅛ teaspoon ground black pepper

HEAT the oil in a large saucepan over medium-high heat. Add the carrot, celery, mushrooms, and garlic. Cook, stirring occasionally, for 5 minutes, or until the vegetables soften. Reduce the heat to medium-low.

ADD the tomatoes and broth. Cover and cook for 5 minutes.

ADD the spinach, parsley, lemon juice, salt, and pepper. Cook for 30 seconds, or until the spinach wilts.

TOTAL TIME: 20 minutes **MAKES 4 SERVINGS**

PER SERVING: 94 calories, 4 g protein, 10 g carbohydrates, 4 g total fat, 1 g saturated fat, 2 g fiber, 414 mg sodium

French-Style Vegetable Soup

To seed tomatoes, cut them in half horizontally. Gently squeeze the halves over a sieve in a bowl. Discard the seeds and reserve the juice for your favorite recipe.

4 cups vegetable or
   chicken broth

2 cups water

1 can (19 ounces) small
   white beans, rinsed
   and drained

1 large tomato, seeded
   and chopped

2 leeks, white and
   pale green parts only,
   thinly sliced

1 small zucchini, thinly sliced

½ pound green beans,
   cut into 1" pieces

4 ounces mushrooms, sliced

1 small butternut squash,
   peeled, seeded, and cubed

2 tablespoons chopped
   fresh parsley or
   1 tablespoon dried

2 teaspoons chopped fresh
   basil or 1 teaspoon dried

2 cloves garlic, minced

½ teaspoon ground
   black pepper

COMBINE the broth, water, white beans, tomato, leeks, zucchini, green beans, mushrooms, squash, parsley, basil, garlic, and pepper in a large saucepan. Bring to a boil over medium-high heat. Reduce the heat to low, cover, and simmer for 12 minutes, or until the vegetables are tender.

TOTAL TIME: 30 minutes MAKES 4 SERVINGS

PER SERVING: 227 calories, 10 g protein, 54 g carbohydrates, 1 g total fat, 0 g saturated fat, 13 g fiber, 882 mg sodium

WHY YOU
SHOULD
CHOOSE

Canned beans

Keep an assortment of black, kidney, cannellini, and pinto beans, as well as chickpeas, handy in the cupboard to add to salads and soups or to puree into dips and spreads. They're high in fiber and protein and reasonable in calories.

Creamy Vegetable Soup

The cannellini beans give this soup a creamy consistency without milk or cream. Feel free to vary the vegetables, depending on what you have on hand. Frozen veggies also work well.

1 tablespoon olive oil

½ onion, chopped

4 large mushrooms, sliced

4 cups low-sodium chicken or vegetable broth

1½ cups broccoli florets

1½ cups cauliflower florets

1 potato, peeled and cubed

1 can (14–19 ounces) cannellini or white beans, rinsed and drained

1 teaspoon salt-free seasoning

¾ cup shredded reduced-fat Cheddar cheese

HEAT the oil in a large saucepan over medium heat. Add the onion and mushrooms. Cook, stirring frequently, for 5 minutes, or until soft.

ADD the broth, broccoli, cauliflower, potato, beans, and seasoning. Cook, covered, for 30 minutes, or until the vegetables are very tender. Remove from the heat.

PUREE the mixture until smooth using an immersion blender, or let cool until lukewarm and puree in a blender. Reheat in the saucepan, if necessary.

DIVIDE the soup among 6 bowls and sprinkle each serving with 2 tablespoons cheese.

TOTAL TIME: 50 minutes **MAKES 6 SERVINGS**

PER SERVING: 156 calories, 10 g protein, 17 g carbohydrates, 6 g total fat, 2 g saturated fat, 4 g fiber, 263 mg sodium

Sweet Potato Soup

A healthy addition to any balanced diet, sweet potatoes are relatively low in calories, high in fiber, and packed with vitamins and minerals. This soup pairs them with apples and a variety of warming spices.

1 tablespoon olive oil

1 large onion, sliced

2 cloves garlic, sliced

1 tablespoon finely chopped fresh ginger

1 teaspoon curry powder

¾ teaspoon ground cumin

½ teaspoon salt

¼ teaspoon ground cinnamon

4 cups water

2 large sweet potatoes, peeled and cut into chunks

3 large Granny Smith apples, peeled, cored, and cut into chunks

½ cup chopped fresh cilantro

HEAT the oil in a large saucepan or Dutch oven over medium heat. Add the onion and garlic and cook, stirring occasionally, for 5 minutes, or until the vegetables soften.

ADD the ginger, curry powder, cumin, salt, and cinnamon. Cook, stirring constantly, for 1 minute. Add the water, sweet potatoes, and apples and bring to a boil over high heat. Reduce the heat to low, cover, and simmer, stirring often, for 20 minutes, or until the sweet potatoes are very tender.

PUREE the mixture until smooth using an immersion blender, or let cool until lukewarm and puree in a blender. Reheat in the saucepan, if necessary. Stir in the cilantro just before serving.

TOTAL TIME: 45 minutes **MAKES 8 SERVINGS**

PER SERVING: 108 calories, 2 g protein, 22 g carbohydrates, 2 g total fat, 0.5 g saturated fat, 3 g fiber, 169 mg sodium

Creamy Potato, Kale, and Leek Soup

Though it is usually available year-round, kale is best during the winter months because it prefers a cold climate. Avoid kale with limp or yellow leaves as this is a sign it's less than fresh.

1 **pound red potatoes**

1 **tablespoon canola oil**

3 **cups chopped and tightly packed kale**

2 **leeks, white and pale green parts only, chopped**

½ **teaspoon salt**

3 **cups 1% milk**

¼ **teaspoon ground nutmeg**

Ground black pepper

CUT the potatoes into golf ball–size pieces and place on a microwaveable plate. Cover with waxed paper. Microwave on high power, rotating occasionally, for 6 minutes, or until tender.

MEANWHILE, heat the oil in a large saucepan over medium heat for 1 minute. Add the kale, leeks, and salt. Cover and cook, stirring occasionally, for 5 minutes, or until the vegetables soften.

ADD the milk, potatoes, and nutmeg. Reduce the heat to medium-low. Smash the potatoes into small chunks with a potato masher or the back of a large spoon. Simmer for 5 minutes. Sprinkle each serving with the pepper.

TOTAL TIME: 25 minutes **MAKES 4 SERVINGS**

PER SERVING: 154 calories, 6 g protein, 24 g carbohydrates, 4 g total fat, 1 g saturated fat, 2 g fiber, 272 mg sodium

Creamy Roasted Garlic Soup

Garlic contains the active compound allicin, which helps fight infection and bacteria. It's little surprise then that garlic has been used for centuries to treat everything from toothaches to open wounds.

1 head garlic, unpeeled

1 tablespoon olive oil

1 large yellow onion, chopped

6 new potatoes, coarsely chopped

1 container (32 ounces) fat-free, reduced-sodium chicken broth

2 carrots, thinly sliced

1 tablespoon chopped fresh rosemary

1 teaspoon dried basil

1 large bunch Swiss chard, stemmed and chopped (8 cups)

1 can (15 ounces) cannellini beans, rinsed and drained

PREHEAT the oven to 425°F. Slice off and discard the top third of the garlic head. Wrap the garlic in foil and roast for 40 minutes. Let cool. Squeeze the roasted garlic from the papery skin into a small bowl and discard the skin.

HEAT the oil in a large saucepan over medium-high heat. Add the onion and cook for 5 minutes, or until translucent. Add the potatoes, broth, and one-third of the garlic. Bring to a boil, reduce the heat, and simmer for 5 minutes.

PUREE the potato mixture until smooth using an immersion blender, or let cool until lukewarm and puree in a blender. Reheat in the saucepan, if necessary.

STIR in the carrots, rosemary, basil, and remaining garlic and cook over medium heat, stirring often, for 10 minutes, or until the carrots are tender.

ADD the chard, return to a simmer, and cook, stirring occasionally, for 5 minutes, or until the chard wilts. Add the beans and cook for 5 minutes, or until heated through.

TOTAL TIME: 1 hour 30 minutes **MAKES 8 SERVINGS**

PER SERVING: 111 calories, 5 g protein, 18 g carbohydrates, 2 g total fat, 0.5 g saturated fat, 4 g fiber, 491 mg sodium

French Onion Soup

Thousands of studies have confirmed many old-time beliefs about the benefits of eating onions. However, their delicious sweet flavor is probably the best reason to enjoy them in this classic soup.

2 tablespoons canola oil

2 large onions, thinly sliced (about 5 cups)

2 bay leaves

1 teaspoon dried thyme

⅛ teaspoon salt

½ cup dry white wine or reduced-sodium vegetable broth

4 cups low-sodium vegetable broth

2 cups water

2 slices (1½ ounces each) whole wheat bread, toasted and halved

1 cup (4 ounces) shredded reduced-fat Swiss cheese

Ground black pepper

PREHEAT the broiler.

HEAT the oil in a large saucepan over medium-high heat. Add the onions, bay leaves, thyme, and salt. Cook, stirring frequently, for 15 minutes, or until the onions are uniformly browned and softened. Reduce the heat, if necessary, to keep the onions from browning too fast.

ADD the wine or ½ cup broth and increase the heat to high. Cook at a brisk simmer for 3 minutes, or until the liquid evaporates. Add the 4 cups broth and water. Bring almost to a boil, reduce the heat, and simmer for 5 minutes. Remove and discard the bay leaves.

PLACE a half slice of toast in the bottom of each of 4 wide, heatproof bowls. Ladle the soup evenly among the bowls. Top each serving with ¼ cup cheese.

BROIL 6" from the heat for 1 minute, or until the cheese is bubbly and light golden brown. Watch very carefully so that the cheese does not burn. Season with the pepper.

TOTAL TIME: 45 minutes **MAKES 4 SERVINGS**

PER SERVING: 278 calories, 12 g protein, 24 g carbohydrates, 14 g total fat, 3 g saturated fat, 4 g fiber, 342 mg sodium

Edamame-Miso Soup

You can find red miso paste in the natural foods section of your supermarket and in health food stores.

¾ cup brown rice

3 cups fat-free, reduced-sodium vegetable broth

2 cups water

1 cup shelled edamame

3 scallions, sliced

2 teaspoons grated fresh ginger

1 clove garlic, minced

2 tablespoons red miso paste

1 carrot, shredded

4 ounces extra-firm tofu, drained and cut into ½" cubes

2 teaspoons less-sodium soy sauce

4 cups fresh baby spinach

COOK the rice according to the package directions.

MEANWHILE, bring the broth and water to a boil in a large saucepan over medium-high heat. Add the edamame, scallions, ginger, and garlic. Reduce the heat to low, cover, and simmer for 10 minutes.

PLACE the miso in a small bowl and stir in some of the hot broth to dissolve the miso. Pour into the broth mixture in the saucepan. Add the carrot, tofu, and soy sauce and cook for 5 minutes. Stir in the spinach. Remove from the heat, cover, and let stand for 3 minutes, or until the spinach wilts.

SPOON ½ cup rice into each of 4 bowls. Divide the soup among the bowls.

TOTAL TIME: 45 minutes **MAKES 4 SERVINGS**

PER SERVING: 233 calories, 12 g protein, 37 g carbohydrates, 5 g total fat, 0.5 g saturated fat, 7 g fiber, 538 mg sodium

Asian Soup with Shrimp Dumplings

Here's a secret for making your dumplings a little easier to form: Moisten your hands first. The same trick works brilliantly for meatballs, too.

4 cloves garlic, smashed and divided

1 (½") piece fresh ginger, peeled, smashed, and divided

½ pound medium shrimp, peeled and deveined

¼ cup chopped fresh cilantro

2 teaspoons cornstarch

2 tablespoons water

1 tablespoon less-sodium soy sauce

½ teaspoon toasted sesame oil

6 cups reduced-sodium chicken broth

1 stalk lemongrass, smashed and tied into a knot

½ teaspoon red-pepper flakes

PLACE half of the garlic and half of the ginger in a food processor and pulse until finely chopped. Add the shrimp and cilantro and pulse to combine. Place the cornstarch in a small bowl and add the water. Stir to dissolve the cornstarch. Add the cornstarch mixture, soy sauce, and oil to the shrimp mixture. Pulse to combine. Set aside.

COMBINE the broth, lemongrass, red-pepper flakes, and the remaining garlic and ginger in a large saucepan over high heat. Bring to a boil. Reduce the heat to low and let simmer.

MEANWHILE, roll the shrimp mixture into 12 balls. Add the dumplings, one at a time, to the soup and simmer for 6 to 7 minutes, or until the dumplings are cooked through. Remove and discard the lemongrass. Ladle the soup into 4 soup bowls and top each with 3 dumplings.

TOTAL TIME: 40 minutes MAKES 4 SERVINGS

PER SERVING: 104 calories, 17 g protein, 5 g carbohydrates, 1 g total fat, 0 g saturated fat, 0 g fiber, 378 mg sodium

Miso-Udon Soup

Miso is a fermented soybean paste commonly used in Japanese cooking. It's sold by color—dark, red, light, and yellow. In delicate soups like this, stick to the light or yellow varieties because they are less salty.

1 package (8 ounces) udon noodles

1 cup chopped asparagus

1 cup frozen snow peas

1 package (14 ounces) tofu, drained and cut into 12 pieces

1 quart low-sodium chicken broth

4 tablespoons light (mellow white) miso

1 cup chopped fresh cilantro

4 scallions, thinly sliced

Less-sodium soy sauce (optional)

COOK the noodles according to the package directions. Add the asparagus and snow peas during the last minute of cooking. Drain and rinse the noodles and vegetables under cold running water. Divide the noodles, vegetables, and tofu among 4 soup bowls.

MEANWHILE, heat the broth in a large saucepan over medium-high heat. Whisk in the miso and bring the mixture to a simmer (do not boil). Ladle the hot broth into the bowls. Top with the cilantro and scallions. Serve with the soy sauce, if desired.

TOTAL TIME: 10 minutes **MAKES 4 SERVINGS**

PER SERVING: 344 calories, 22 g protein, 52 g carbohydrates, 5 g total fat, 0.5 g saturated fat, 8 g fiber, 700 mg sodium

WHY YOU SHOULD CHOOSE

Tofu

It is an incredibly versatile ingredient. Made from soybeans, tofu comes in a wide range of forms—extra-firm for stir-frying, soft silken, seasoned and ready-to-use, and even firm (Chinese) and soft (Japanese) noodles.

Updated Chicken Noodle Soup

When chicken is cooked, it releases chemicals that resemble the bronchitis drug acetylcysteine (Acetadote). This may help explain why chicken soup has such legendary cold-fighting benefits. The soup's salty broth keeps mucus thin the same way cough medicines do.

2 tablespoons canola oil

¾ pound boneless, skinless chicken breast, cut into 1" strips

1 large onion, chopped

2 cloves garlic, chopped

5 cups fat-free, reduced-sodium chicken broth

1 cup water

3 cups broccoli florets

2 carrots, chopped

2 teaspoons grated fresh ginger

8 ounces whole grain rotini

HEAT the oil in a large saucepan over medium-high heat. Add the chicken and cook, stirring occasionally, for 5 minutes, or until browned. Remove to a bowl with a slotted spoon. Keep warm.

ADD the onion to the saucepan and cook for 5 minutes, or until lightly browned. Add the garlic and cook for 1 minute. Add the broth, water, broccoli, carrots, and ginger and bring to a boil. Stir in the pasta and cook for 11 minutes, or until tender. Add the chicken back to the soup during the last 2 to 3 minutes of cooking.

TOTAL TIME: 50 minutes **MAKES 6 SERVINGS**

PER SERVING: 276 calories, 22 g protein, 31 g carbohydrates, 8 g total fat, 1 g saturated fat, 7 g fiber, 448 mg sodium

Chicken Dumpling Soup

Frozen vegetables, biscuit mix, and a slow cooker are your secret weapons for preparing this simple version of a timeless dish.

1 pound boneless, skinless chicken breasts, cut into ½" pieces

2 cans (14.5 ounces each) fat-free, reduced-sodium chicken broth

1 package (10 ounces) frozen mixed vegetables

1 onion, chopped

1½ cups biscuit or all-purpose baking mix

½ cup 1% milk

Ground black pepper (optional)

PLACE the chicken, broth, mixed vegetables, and onion in a 4-quart or larger slow cooker. Stir to combine.

COOK, covered, on low for 5 hours, or on high for 2½ hours.

COMBINE the biscuit mix and milk in a large bowl. Drop by rounded tablespoonfuls into the soup. Cover and cook on high for 1 hour. Garnish with the pepper, if desired.

TOTAL TIME: 6 hours 15 minutes **MAKES 4 SERVINGS**

PER SERVING: 250 calories, 26 g protein, 32 g carbohydrates, 3 g total fat, 1 g saturated fat, 4 g fiber, 418 mg sodium

Russian Beet and Bean Soup

This soup is great served hot or chilled. If you make it ahead of time, taste and adjust the seasoning just before serving, adding a drizzle of vinegar or a pinch of fresh dill, if needed.

1 teaspoon olive oil

2 small onions, finely chopped

2 cloves garlic, finely chopped

3 cups chicken broth

1 cup no-salt-added tomato puree

3 beets, peeled and chopped

2 tablespoons honey

½ teaspoon dried thyme

6 ounces beet greens, chopped

1 can (15 ounces) kidney beans, rinsed and drained

2 tablespoons cider vinegar

¼ teaspoon salt

1 tablespoon chopped fresh dill or 1 teaspoon dried

3 tablespoons 0% plain Greek yogurt

HEAT the oil in a large saucepan over medium-high heat. Add the onions and garlic. Cook, stirring occasionally, for 5 minutes, or until soft.

ADD the broth, tomato puree, beets, honey, and thyme. Bring to a boil. Reduce the heat to low, cover, and simmer for 30 minutes, or until the beets are very soft when pierced with a sharp knife.

STIR in the beet greens, beans, vinegar, and salt. Simmer for 10 minutes, or until the greens are tender. Stir in the dill. Ladle the soup into 6 bowls and top each serving with ½ tablespoon yogurt.

TOTAL TIME: 1 hour **MAKES 6 SERVINGS**

PER SERVING: 140 calories, 7 g protein, 28 g carbohydrates, 1 g total fat, 0 g saturated fat, 6 g fiber, 615 mg sodium

Mushroom-Barley Soup with Spinach and Sausage

Rich and meaty mushrooms, as well as a few soy sausages, transform this humble barley soup into a deliciously hearty dish. Serve with a small piece of crusty bread and a simple green salad for an easy weeknight dinner.

- **3** cups water, divided
- **1** ounce dried porcini mushrooms
- **2** teaspoons olive oil
- **2** (4 ounces each) frozen soy sausage links
- **8** ounces cremini mushrooms, sliced
- **2** shallots, finely chopped
- **2** carrots, chopped
- **2** ribs celery, chopped
- **1** cup quick-cooking barley
- **2** cloves garlic, minced
- **1** teaspoon dried thyme
- **1** container (32 ounces) reduced-sodium beef or vegetable broth
- **1** package (7–9 ounces) fresh baby spinach

BRING 1 cup of the water to a boil. Place the porcini mushrooms in a medium bowl, add the boiling water, and soak for 30 minutes.

MEANWHILE, heat the oil in a large saucepan or Dutch oven over medium heat. Cook the sausages, turning occasionally, for 8 minutes, or until browned. Remove to a plate, chop into bite-size pieces, and set aside.

COAT the same pan with cooking spray and place over medium-high heat. Cook the brown mushrooms, shallots, carrots, and celery, stirring occasionally, for 10 minutes, or until browned. Add the barley, garlic, and thyme and cook, stirring occasionally, for 2 minutes.

REMOVE the porcini mushrooms from the liquid, reserving the liquid. Chop the mushrooms and add to the pan. Stir in the broth, reserved liquid, and remaining 2 cups water. Bring to a boil. Reduce the heat to low, cover, and simmer for 10 minutes, or until the barley is tender.

STIR in the spinach and sausage. Cook for 2 minutes, or until the spinach wilts.

TOTAL TIME: 1 hour 15 minutes **MAKES 4 SERVINGS**

PER SERVING: 311 calories, 22 g protein, 53 g carbohydrates, 3 g total fat, 0.5 g saturated fat, 10 g fiber, 862 mg sodium

Easy Corn Chowder

Just a few basic ingredients go into the slow cooker to make this simple corn chowder. Blend half of the batch until smooth and creamy to give the soup its signature texture.

3 potatoes, peeled and cut into ½" pieces

2 cans (15 ounces each) whole kernel corn, drained

1 onion, chopped

2 cups low-sodium chicken broth

2 cups 1% milk

¼ cup trans-free margarine

Chopped fresh chives (optional)

PLACE the potatoes, corn, onion, and broth in a 4-quart or larger slow cooker. Stir to combine.

COOK, covered, on low for 7 to 9 hours. Let cool for 10 minutes.

TRANSFER half of the corn mixture to a blender and process until smooth (remove the center piece of the blender lid and cover with a towel so steam can escape). Return the pureed mixture to the cooker and stir in the milk and margarine. Cover and cook on high for 1 hour. Garnish with chives, if desired.

TOTAL TIME: 8 hours 30 minutes **MAKES 6 SERVINGS**

PER SERVING: 283 calories, 8 g protein, 36 g carbohydrates, 8 g total fat, 2.5 g saturated fat, 3 g fiber, 456 mg sodium

Chickpea Stew

The spiciness of curry combined with the creaminess of coconut milk makes this stew simply irresistible on a cold, blustery day.

- **2 tablespoons canola oil**
- **1 onion, chopped**
- **2 tablespoons curry powder**
- **2 teaspoons ground cumin**
- **¼ teaspoon salt**
- **1 quart low-sodium vegetable broth**
- **1 large sweet potato, chopped**
- **1 can (15 ounces) chickpeas, rinsed and drained**
- **1 can (14.5 ounces) no-salt-added petite-cut diced tomatoes**
- **1 cup light coconut milk**
- **2 tablespoons finely chopped fresh cilantro**
- **½ teaspoon ground black pepper**

HEAT the oil in a large saucepan over medium heat. Add the onion. Cook, stirring occasionally, for 10 minutes, or until very soft.

STIR in the curry powder, cumin, and salt. Cook for 2 minutes, or until fragrant. Add the broth and sweet potato and bring to a boil. Reduce the heat, cover, and simmer for 15 minutes, or until the potato is tender.

STIR in the chickpeas, tomatoes, and coconut milk. Cover and simmer for 10 minutes, or until heated through. Stir in the cilantro and pepper just before serving.

TOTAL TIME: 50 minutes **MAKES 4 SERVINGS**

PER SERVING: 306 calories, 7 g protein, 42 g carbohydrates, 13 g total fat, 4 g saturated fat, 8 g fiber, 556 mg sodium

Tuscan Chicken Soup

A hearty, colorful stew like this one makes use of what's in your fridge and pantry and helps you meet your daily quota for optimal health.

2 **carrots, chopped**

1 **rib celery, chopped**

¼ **cup water**

2 **tablespoons olive oil**

1 **onion, chopped**

4 **large cloves garlic, minced**

1 **large bay leaf**

8 **cups low-sodium chicken broth**

3 **cups shredded roasted skinless chicken breast**

3 **plum tomatoes, chopped**

1 **small zucchini, grated**

1 **can (15 ounces) no-salt-added cannellini beans, rinsed and drained**

1 **can (14 ounces) artichoke hearts in water, rinsed, drained, and roughly chopped**

½ **teaspoon dried oregano**

½ **teaspoon dried sage**

½ **teaspoon dried thyme**

12 **thin slices Parmesan cheese, cut with a vegetable peeler (optional)**

PLACE the carrots and celery in a small microwaveable bowl. Add the water and cover the top of the bowl loosely with plastic wrap. Microwave on high power for 5 minutes, or until the vegetables are almost tender.

HEAT the oil in a saucepan over medium heat. Add the onion and cook for 5 to 7 minutes, or until soft. Add the garlic and cook for 1 to 2 minutes, or until fragrant. Add the steamed vegetables and bay leaf. Cook for 4 to 5 minutes.

ADD the broth, chicken, tomatoes, zucchini, beans, and artichoke hearts. Reduce the heat and simmer for 30 minutes. Remove and discard the bay leaf. Add the oregano, sage, and thyme and simmer for 5 minutes. Ladle the soup into 6 bowls. Top each bowl with 2 slices of cheese, if desired.

TOTAL TIME: 1 hour 30 minutes **MAKES 6 SERVINGS**

PER SERVING: 278 calories, 32 g protein, 18 g carbohydrates, 8 g total fat, 2 g saturated fat, 5 g fiber, 525 mg sodium

Tortilla Soup

Here's a fun soup for a casual get-together with friends. Provide a variety of toppings so guests can customize their own bowls.

1 tablespoon canola oil

1 onion, chopped

2 cloves garlic, chopped

1 can (14 ounces) whole peeled tomatoes

1 tablespoon chopped chipotle pepper in adobo sauce

6 cups chicken broth

2 boneless, skinless chicken breast halves (6 ounces each)

2 corn tortillas (6" diameter), cut into strips

¼ cup fresh lime juice (2 limes)

Hot sauce (optional)

½ avocado, peeled, pitted, and chopped

Chopped onion, pickled jalapeño chile peppers, sliced radishes, fresh cilantro (optional)

HEAT the oil in a large saucepan over medium heat. Add the onion and garlic and cook until soft, about 5 minutes. Add the tomatoes (with juice) and chipotle pepper.

PUREE the mixture until smooth using an immersion blender, or transfer to a food processor or blender and puree until smooth. Return to the saucepan, if necessary.

ADD the broth and bring to a simmer. Add the chicken breasts to the simmering soup and poach for 10 minutes, or until cooked through. Remove the chicken to a plate and set aside.

PREHEAT the oven to 450°F. Lay the tortilla strips on a baking sheet and bake for 3 to 5 minutes, or until lightly browned and crispy.

SEASON the soup with the lime juice and adjust the seasoning with hot sauce, if using. Thinly slice the chicken. Divide the soup among 4 warm bowls. Top with the chicken, tortilla strips, avocado, and other desired toppings.

TOTAL TIME: 35 minutes **MAKES 4 SERVINGS**

PER SERVING: 347 calories, 31 g protein, 29 g carbohydrates, 12 g total fat, 2 g saturated fat, 4 g fiber, 755 mg sodium

Black Soybean Chili

This unique chili can hold its own against more expected renditions on game day. In fact, the toothsome texture of hominy might even give it an edge.

2 tablespoons olive oil

1 large onion, chopped

1 large carrot, chopped

3 cloves garlic, chopped

2 cans (15 ounces each) black soybeans, rinsed and drained

1 can (15 ounces) hominy, rinsed and drained

1 can (28 ounces) crushed tomatoes

1 tablespoon ancho chili powder

1 teaspoon salt

¼ cup chopped fresh cilantro

HEAT the oil in a large saucepan over medium-high heat. Add the onion, carrot, and garlic. Cook, stirring occasionally, for 10 minutes, or until very soft.

ADD the soybeans, hominy, tomatoes, chili powder, and salt. Bring to a boil. Reduce the heat to low, cover, and simmer for 30 minutes. Stir in the cilantro just before serving.

TOTAL TIME: 50 minutes   **MAKES 6 SERVINGS**

PER SERVING: 218 calories, 11 g protein, 26 g carbohydrates, 10 g total fat, 1.5 g saturated fat, 9 g fiber, 691 mg sodium

Chicken Jambalaya

Any combination of meats can be used in this traditional New Orleans favorite, but sticking to chicken breast and poultry sausage makes this dish a hands-down winner for weight loss.

½ **red bell pepper, seeded and chopped**

4 **scallions, sliced**

3 **cloves garlic, minced**

2 **teaspoons Creole seasoning**

1 **teaspoon canola oil**

1 **can (14 ounces) no-salt-added diced tomatoes**

1 **cup canned no-salt-added small red beans, rinsed and drained**

⅛ **teaspoon salt**

½ **pound boneless, skinless chicken breast, cut into ¼"-thick strips**

4 **ounces reduced-fat Italian chicken or turkey sausage, cut into 8 pieces**

3 **tablespoons quick-cooking brown rice**

Hot-pepper sauce

COMBINE the bell pepper, scallions, garlic, seasoning, and oil in a deep, wide nonstick skillet. Cover and cook over medium heat, stirring occasionally, for 5 minutes, or until the pepper starts to soften. Reduce the heat if the pepper starts to brown.

ADD the tomatoes, beans, and salt to the skillet. Stir to combine. Simmer for 5 minutes.

ADD the chicken, sausage, and rice, spooning some of the tomatoes on top. Cover and simmer for 10 minutes, or until the chicken is no longer pink and the rice is tender. Remove from the heat and let stand, covered, for 5 minutes. Serve with hot-pepper sauce at the table.

TOTAL TIME: 50 minutes **MAKES 4 SERVINGS**

PER SERVING: 217 calories, 23 g protein, 18 g carbohydrates, 5 g total fat, 0 g saturated fat, 4 g fiber, 549 mg sodium

Chipotle Beef Stew

Look for ground chipotle, which is made from dried smoked jalapeño chile peppers, in the spice section of the supermarket. Ground red pepper can be used if chipotle is not available. If using the low-heat setting on your slow cooker, cook the stew for 6 hours.

1½ **pounds lean beef stew meat, cubed**

½ **cup sliced onion**

2 **tablespoons all-purpose flour**

1 **tablespoon minced garlic**

¼–½ **teaspoon ground chipotle, divided**

¼ **teaspoon ground cumin**

¼ **teaspoon dried oregano**

¼ **teaspoon salt**

½ **cup strong brewed coffee**

½ **cup canned diced tomatoes with juice**

Chopped fresh cilantro (optional)

COMBINE the beef, onion, flour, garlic, ¼ teaspoon of the chipotle, cumin, oregano, and salt in a 4-quart or larger slow cooker. Stir to coat the beef evenly with the other ingredients. Add the coffee and tomatoes.

COOK, covered, on high for 3 hours, or until the beef is fork-tender.

TASTE and add up to ¼ teaspoon of the remaining chipotle, if desired. Garnish with cilantro, if using.

TOTAL TIME: 3 hours 10 minutes **MAKES 6 SERVINGS**

PER SERVING: 185 calories, 26 g protein, 4 g carbohydrates, 6 g total fat, 2 g saturated fat, 1 g fiber, 210 mg sodium

Salads

CHAPTER

8

Caesar Salad

Traditional Caesar salads call for uncooked eggs, which present some risk of food-borne illness. Using pasteurized egg products instead solves the problem.

¼ cup pasteurized liquid egg substitute

1 clove garlic, minced

1½ teaspoons anchovy paste

½ teaspoon Dijon mustard

¼ teaspoon Worcestershire sauce

2 tablespoons fresh lemon juice

2 tablespoons olive oil

8 cups coarsely torn romaine lettuce

2 hard-cooked eggs, peeled and chopped

¼ cup shaved Parmesan cheese

½ cup croutons

WHISK together the egg substitute, garlic, anchovy paste, mustard, Worcestershire sauce, and lemon juice in a large bowl. Slowly add the oil in a steady stream, whisking until combined.

ADD the lettuce to the dressing and toss to coat. Top with the eggs, cheese, and croutons.

TOTAL TIME: 10 minutes **MAKES 4 SERVINGS**

PER SERVING: 178 calories, 9 g protein, 8 g carbohydrates, 13 g total fat, 3 g saturated fat, 2 g fiber, 355 mg sodium

Heirloom Tomato and Peach Salad

Bursting with the taste of summer, this salad has no need for greens. But if you prefer, serve it over a bed of baby arugula.

- **6** heirloom tomatoes, such as Green Zebra
- **3** large yellow peaches
- **3** ounces fresh mozzarella cheese, cubed
- **⅓** cup small or torn fresh basil leaves
- **4** teaspoons basil oil or olive oil
- **¼** teaspoon salt
- **¼** teaspoon ground black pepper

CHOP the tomatoes and peaches into ½" pieces. Toss with the cheese, basil, oil, salt, and pepper in a large bowl.

TOTAL TIME: 10 minutes **MAKES 4 SERVINGS**

PER SERVING: 194 calories, 7 g protein, 22 g carbohydrates, 10 g total fat, 4 g saturated fat, 4 g fiber, 182 mg sodium

Herbed Salad with Walnuts

Walnuts add a nice crunch to this otherwise delicate salad. For a more pronounced walnut flavor, substitute 2 tablespoons of walnut oil for the same amount of olive oil.

¼ **cup roughly chopped walnuts**

6 **tablespoons olive oil**

2 **tablespoons white wine vinegar**

¾ **teaspoon salt**

8 **cups salad greens**

½ **cup chopped fresh herbs, such as chives, basil, and/or parsley**

TOAST the walnuts in a small dry skillet over medium-high heat for 5 minutes, or until fragrant. Place on a plate and set aside.

WHISK together the oil, vinegar, and salt in a large bowl. Add the greens and herbs and toss to coat.

TOP each serving with the walnuts.

TOTAL TIME: 10 minutes **MAKES 4 SERVINGS**

PER SERVING: 240 calories, 3 g protein, 3 g carbohydrates, 25 g total fat, 3 g saturated fat, 2 g fiber, 2 mg sodium

Vegetarian Cobb Salad

This salad is every bit as colorful and delicious as the original Cobb salad. If you miss the flavor of bacon and still want to enjoy a meatless dish, look for smoked mozzarella to use in this recipe instead of regular mozzarella.

10 cups mixed baby greens

4 ounces part-skim mozzarella cheese, chopped

4 hard-cooked eggs, peeled and chopped

2 plum tomatoes, chopped

1 avocado, peeled, pitted, and chopped

½ small red onion, chopped

1 cup coarsely crumbled pita chips

½ cup bottled reduced-calorie blue cheese dressing

ARRANGE the greens on a large serving platter and top with the cheese, eggs, tomatoes, avocado, and onion. Scatter the pita chips over the length of the salad and serve with the dressing.

TOTAL TIME: 15 minutes **MAKES 4 SERVINGS**

PER SERVING: 314 calories, 18 g protein, 22 g carbohydrates, 18 g total fat, 5.5 g saturated fat, 6 g fiber, 883 mg sodium

Chickpea and Roasted Tomato Salad

Also known as garbanzo beans, chickpeas are one of the oldest cultivated food crops known to man. Because the dried beans require a long cooking time, the canned version remains an attractive option for the modern cook.

8 plum tomatoes, halved and cored

8 scallions, cut into 2" pieces

2 tablespoons canola oil

¼ teaspoon salt

1 bag (6 ounces) fresh baby spinach

1 can (15 ounces) chickpeas, rinsed and drained

2 tablespoons balsamic vinegar

PREHEAT the oven to 425°F.

PLACE the tomatoes and scallions on a large rimmed baking sheet. Drizzle with the oil and sprinkle with the salt. Toss to coat. Roast for 10 minutes, or until browned and tender. Let cool slightly.

MEANWHILE, place the spinach and chickpeas in a large bowl. Top with the tomato mixture and drizzle with the vinegar. Toss to coat. Serve immediately.

TOTAL TIME: 20 minutes MAKES 4 SERVINGS

PER SERVING: 179 calories, 6 g protein, 23 g carbohydrates, 4 g total fat, 0.5 g saturated fat, 7 g fiber, 306 mg sodium

Eggplant and Chickpea Salad with Cherry Tomatoes

For the best-tasting eggplant, check out its "belly button" (an oval or round dimple at the blossom end). Buy only eggplants with oval dimples—the round ones tend to mean there will be more seeds and less "meat." For this particular recipe, look for grilled eggplant at your grocer's salad or olive bar where other roasted vegetables are sold.

4 cups cubed (½") grilled eggplant (8 large slices)

2 cans (15 ounces each) no-salt-added chickpeas, rinsed and drained

1 cup cherry tomatoes, cut crosswise into ¼"-thick slices

1 tablespoon finely chopped fresh parsley

2 tablespoons red wine vinegar

2 tablespoons olive oil

1 tablespoon lemon juice

2 cloves garlic, minced

½ teaspoon grated lemon peel

¼ teaspoon ground black pepper

TOSS the eggplant, chickpeas, tomatoes, and parsley in a large bowl.

WHISK the vinegar, oil, lemon juice, garlic, lemon peel, and pepper in a small bowl. Pour over the salad and toss gently to coat. Let stand for at least 20 minutes at room temperature (chill if left standing for more than 2 hours).

TOTAL TIME: 35 minutes **MAKES 8 SERVINGS**

PER SERVING: 252 calories, 8 g protein, 32 g carbohydrates, 12 g total fat, 2 g saturated fat, 12 g fiber, 509 mg sodium

Chickpea and Arugula Salad

Arugula is an aromatic salad green with a distinct peppery flavor. Like most greens, it is very low in calories, making it an excellent (as well as delicious) main ingredient to aid your weight loss efforts.

10 cups arugula

1 can (15 ounces) chickpeas, rinsed and drained

½ small red onion, sliced

2 large carrots, shredded

¼ cup olive oil

¼ teaspoon salt

Ground black pepper

2 tablespoons cider vinegar

COMBINE the arugula, chickpeas, onion, and carrots in a large bowl. Drizzle with the oil and sprinkle with the salt and a few grinds of pepper. Use your hands to toss thoroughly. Drizzle with the vinegar. Toss again and serve.

TOTAL TIME: 10 minutes **MAKES 4 SERVINGS**

PER SERVING: 234 calories, 5 g protein, 22 g carbohydrates, 15 g total fat, 2 g saturated fat, 5 g fiber, 391 mg sodium

Spinach Salad with Avocado, Fresh Mozzarella, and Strawberry Dressing

Not a strawberry fan? Prepare the dressing with raspberries instead and skip the strawberries altogether.

- 3 tablespoons chopped almonds
- 2 cups hulled and sliced strawberries, divided
- 2 tablespoons olive oil
- 2 tablespoons honey
- 1 tablespoon + 1 teaspoon balsamic vinegar
- ½ teaspoon salt
- ⅛ teaspoon ground black pepper
- 1 bag (6 ounces) fresh baby spinach
- 1 ripe mango, peeled, seeded, and chopped
- 5 ounces fresh mozzarella cheese, chopped
- 1 ripe avocado, peeled, pitted, and chopped

TOAST the almonds in a small dry skillet over medium-high heat for 5 minutes, or until fragrant. Place on a plate and set aside.

COMBINE ½ cup of the strawberries, the oil, honey, and vinegar in a food processor. Process until smooth. Scrape into a large salad bowl and stir in the salt and pepper.

ADD the spinach, mango, and remaining 1½ cups strawberries to the dressing and toss to coat. Sprinkle the cheese, avocado, and toasted almonds over the top.

TOTAL TIME: 25 minutes **MAKES 4 SERVINGS**

PER SERVING: 364 calories, 10 g protein, 27 g carbohydrates, 26 g total fat, 7 g saturated fat, 8 g fiber, 387 mg sodium

Spiced-Up Spinach Salad

Toasting the nuts in the oven keeps the pepper coating intact. If you prefer less spice, simply toast the nuts in a skillet on the stove as instructed in other recipes in this book.

½ cup walnuts, coarsely chopped

1 teaspoon + ⅛ teaspoon ground black pepper

1 tablespoon balsamic vinegar

2 teaspoons Dijon mustard

2 teaspoons honey

⅛ teaspoon salt

⅓ cup 0% plain Greek yogurt

1 bag (6 ounces) fresh baby spinach

¼ cup dried cranberries

PREHEAT the oven to 400°F. Coat a small baking sheet with cooking spray. Place the walnuts on the baking sheet and coat with cooking spray. Sprinkle with 1 teaspoon of the pepper and bake for 8 minutes, or until toasted.

MEANWHILE, whisk together the vinegar, mustard, honey, salt, and remaining ⅛ teaspoon pepper in a small bowl. Stir in the yogurt.

COMBINE the spinach, cranberries, walnuts, and yogurt mixture in a large bowl. Toss to coat.

TOTAL TIME: 20 minutes **MAKES 4 SERVINGS**

PER SERVING: 165 calories, 5 g protein, 19 g carbohydrates, 10 g total fat, 1 g saturated fat, 4 g fiber, 234 mg sodium

Watermelon Salad

When fresh, watermelon is approximately 92 percent water, so look for ones that feel heavy for their size. Also, check the underside of the watermelon for a creamy yellow spot. That's a sign that it's been sitting on the ground, ripening in the sun.

¼ cup pecans

4 cups fresh baby spinach

2 cups chopped watermelon

¼ cup crumbled feta cheese

1 tablespoon chopped fresh mint

2 tablespoons bottled raspberry vinaigrette

TOAST the pecans in a small dry skillet over medium-high heat for 5 minutes, or until fragrant. Place on a plate and set aside.

COMBINE the spinach, watermelon, cheese, and mint in a large bowl. Drizzle with the vinaigrette. Toss to coat. Sprinkle the toasted pecans over the top.

TOTAL TIME: 15 minutes **MAKES 2 SERVINGS**

PER SERVING: 267 calories, 7 g protein, 35 g carbohydrates, 14 g total fat, 4 g saturated fat, 5 g fiber, 320 mg sodium

Edamame and Wild Rice Salad

The nutty flavor of prepared goddess salad dressing is a perfect complement to the wild rice and cashews in this salad, but if it is hard to find at your grocery, any sesame-ginger dressing would be a good substitute.

¼ cup wild rice

⅓ cup frozen shelled edamame

1 cup frozen Chinese stir-fry vegetables

2 tablespoons bottled goddess dressing

2 tablespoons cashews

COOK the wild rice according to the package directions.

THAW the edamame and stir-fry vegetables in a colander under warm running water. Drain well.

TOSS the rice and vegetables with the dressing in a bowl and sprinkle with the cashews. Serve warm or at room temperature.

TOTAL TIME: 10 minutes **MAKES 1 SERVING**

PER SERVING: 360 calories, 12 g protein, 29 g carbohydrates, 23 g total fat, 3 g saturated fat, 6 g fiber, 300 mg sodium

Edamame and Soba Salad

Soba noodles are thin, chewy buckwheat noodles and a mainstay ingredient in the Japanese diet. Serve this salad either warm or cold, depending on the season and your preference.

4 ounces soba noodles

⅔ cup frozen shelled edamame

¼ cup orange juice

¼ cup tahini

1 tablespoon toasted sesame oil

1 tablespoon white vinegar

2 teaspoons soy sauce

1 package (14 ounces) tofu, drained and cubed

2 cups bean sprouts

1 large cucumber, thinly sliced

4 cups fresh baby spinach

½ teaspoon red-pepper flakes

PREPARE the noodles according to the package directions, adding the edamame after 1 minute. Drain well. If preparing a cold noodle salad, rinse under cold running water and drain well again.

WHISK together the orange juice, tahini, oil, vinegar, and soy sauce in a large bowl. Add the noodles and edamame, tofu, bean sprouts, cucumber, and spinach. Toss to coat. Sprinkle with the red-pepper flakes.

TOTAL TIME: 20 minutes **MAKES 4 SERVINGS**

PER SERVING: 416 calories, 26 g protein, 41 g carbohydrates, 20 g total fat, 3 g saturated fat, 7 g fiber, 513 mg sodium

Asian Chicken and Melon Salad

If you're a seafood fan, you might enjoy this salad with grilled shrimp in place of the chicken.

2 cups sugar snap peas or snow peas, strings removed and halved

2 tablespoons chopped fresh cilantro

1½ tablespoons lime juice

1 tablespoon water

2 teaspoons toasted sesame oil

1 teaspoon grated fresh ginger

⅛ teaspoon salt

2 cups honeydew melon balls

1½ cups shredded cooked skinless chicken breast

1 red bell pepper, seeded and cut into thin, short strips

1 bag (5 ounces) fresh baby spinach

¼ cup unsalted dry-roasted cashews (optional)

BRING a small saucepan of water to a boil over high heat. Cook the sugar snap peas or snow peas for 4 minutes, or until tender-crisp. Drain and rinse under cold running water. Drain well.

WHISK together the cilantro, lime juice, water, oil, ginger, and salt in a large bowl. Add the melon, chicken, bell pepper, spinach, and peas. Toss to coat. Divide among 4 plates and sprinkle with the cashews, if using.

TOTAL TIME: 25 minutes **MAKES 4 SERVINGS**

PER SERVING: 267 calories, 21 g protein, 23 g carbohydrates, 11 g total fat, 2 g saturated fat, 5 g fiber, 162 mg sodium

Chicken Waldorf Salad

This chicken salad for one travels well if you keep it cold and store the oil and vinegar dressing in a separate container. Toss the dressing with the rest of the ingredients right before lunchtime.

2 teaspoons olive oil

2 teaspoons red wine vinegar

¼ teaspoon ground black pepper

2 ribs celery, chopped

1 small apple, chopped

1 cup fresh spinach

¾ cup chopped cooked skinless chicken breast

¼ cup whole wheat croutons

1 tablespoon chopped walnuts

WHISK together the oil, vinegar, and pepper in a medium bowl. Stir in the celery, apple, spinach, chicken, croutons, and walnuts.

TOTAL TIME: 10 minutes MAKES 1 SERVING

PER SERVING: 399 calories, 30 g protein, 31 g carbohydrates, 18 g total fat, 3 g saturated fat, 6 g fiber, 206 mg sodium

Chinese Chicken Salad

Crispy wonton wrappers are a fun alternative to croutons in this light, refreshing salad. Baking them yourself lets you control the fat and calories in the final dish.

12 square wonton wrappers

4 cups mesclun or torn romaine lettuce

2 cups chopped cooked skinless chicken breast

½ package (about 3½ ounces) enoki mushrooms

1 can sliced water chestnuts, drained

3 scallions, thinly sliced

1 rib celery, chopped

2 tablespoons rice vinegar

1 tablespoon peanut oil

1 tablespoon sesame seeds

1 tablespoon hoisin sauce

1 teaspoon sesame oil

1 teaspoon mustard powder

½ teaspoon sriracha sauce (optional)

PREHEAT the oven to 350°F. Cut the wonton wrappers into ½"-wide strips. Place the strips on a nonstick baking sheet. Coat with cooking spray and bake for 5 minutes, or until crisp and lightly browned.

COMBINE the lettuce, chicken, mushrooms, water chestnuts, scallions, and celery in a large salad bowl.

WHISK together the vinegar, peanut oil, sesame seeds, hoisin sauce, sesame oil, mustard powder, and sriracha sauce (if using) in a small bowl. Pour over the salad. Toss to coat. Top with the crisp wonton strips.

TOTAL TIME: 20 minutes **MAKES 4 SERVINGS**

PER SERVING: 305 calories, 23 g protein, 28 g carbohydrates, 12 g total fat, 2 g saturated fat, 6 g fiber, 276 mg sodium

Date-Nut Chicken Salad

Use Medjool dates in this salad if you can. Their sweet, chewy texture is the perfect contrast to the crunchy walnuts.

¼ cup walnuts, chopped

8 cups mixed greens

1 grilled skinless chicken breast half (8 ounces), chopped

4 ounces goat cheese, crumbled

¼ cup chopped dates

¼ cup bottled low-fat balsamic vinaigrette

TOAST the walnuts in a small dry skillet over medium-high heat for 5 minutes, or until fragrant. Place on a plate and set aside.

COMBINE the greens, chicken, goat cheese, dates, and vinaigrette in a large bowl and toss gently to coat. Divide among 4 plates and sprinkle with the toasted walnuts.

TOTAL TIME: 15 minutes MAKES 4 SERVINGS

PER SERVING: 296 calories, 27 g protein, 16 g carbohydrates, 16 g total fat, 7 g saturated fat, 4 g fiber, 234 mg sodium

Chopped Moroccan Salad

Inspired by the intensely spicy, stewed dishes of Morocco known as *tagines*, this salad provides the same flavor profile with considerably more texture thanks to all the fresh ingredients.

2 tablespoons lime juice

1 tablespoon honey

1 tablespoon olive oil

½ teaspoon grated orange peel

¼ teaspoon ground cumin

Generous pinch of ground cinnamon

3 cups baby arugula

1 yellow tomato, chopped

1 cup chopped grilled skinless chicken breast

½ cucumber, peeled and chopped

¼ avocado, peeled, pitted, and chopped

½ cup canned no-salt-added chickpeas, rinsed and drained

¼ cup golden raisins

2 tablespoons chopped red onion

2 teaspoons sunflower seeds

COMBINE the lime juice, honey, oil, orange peel, cumin, and cinnamon in a blender or food processor and process until smooth, or whisk together in a small bowl.

COMBINE the arugula, tomato, chicken, cucumber, avocado, chickpeas, raisins, onion, and dressing in a large bowl and toss gently to coat. Top with the sunflower seeds.

TOTAL TIME: 25 minutes **MAKES 2 SERVINGS**

PER SERVING: 419 calories, 25 g protein, 49 g carbohydrates, 16 g total fat, 2 g saturated fat, 7 g fiber, 318 mg sodium

Crispy Chicken Salad

Incorporate the classic flavors of chicken cordon bleu into an elegant salad with this recipe.

- 2 boneless, skinless chicken breast halves (8 ounces each)
- ¼ teaspoon ground black pepper
- 2 slices (1 ounce each) reduced-sodium deli ham
- 2 slices (1 ounce each) reduced-fat Swiss cheese
- 1 egg white, beaten
- 1 cup panko bread crumbs
- 4 cups baby arugula
- ½ cup grape tomatoes, quartered
- 1 lemon, cut into wedges

PREHEAT the oven to 425°F. Lightly oil a baking sheet.

SLICE each chicken breast half into 2 thin, flat pieces by laying it on a flat surface, placing your hand on top, and sliding a knife blade evenly through the breast parallel with the work surface.

SEASON the chicken with the pepper. Cut the ham and cheese slices in half and arrange on top of each piece of chicken. Beginning at a short side, roll up each piece of chicken, securing with a wooden pick.

PLACE the egg white and panko in separate shallow bowls. Dip each chicken roll in the egg white and then the panko to coat. Place on the baking sheet.

BAKE for 15 to 20 minutes, turning once, or until golden brown and cooked through. Remove the wooden picks and cut the chicken into slices. Divide the arugula, tomatoes, and chicken among 4 plates. Squeeze a lemon wedge over each serving.

TOTAL TIME: 30 minutes **MAKES 4 SERVINGS**

PER SERVING: 236 calories, 33 g protein, 15 g carbohydrates, 4 g total fat, 1 g saturated fat, 1 g fiber, 327 mg sodium

Quick and Crunchy Chef Salad

On days when you're craving something crunchy, this salad is incredibly satisfying. The toasted sunflower seeds are a great alternative to croutons.

4 cups chopped
  romaine lettuce

1 cup cherry tomatoes,
  halved

1 grilled boneless, skinless
  chicken breast half
  (about 6 ounces), chopped

¼ cup shredded reduced-fat
  Cheddar cheese

¼ small red onion,
  finely chopped

2 tablespoons bottled
  balsamic vinaigrette

2 tablespoons toasted
  sunflower seeds

COMBINE the lettuce, tomatoes, chicken, cheese, onion, and vinaigrette in a large bowl and toss gently to coat. Top with the sunflower seeds.

TOTAL TIME: 10 minutes **MAKES 2 SERVINGS**

PER SERVING: 310 calories, 33 g protein, 11 g carbohydrates, 15 g total fat, 3 g saturated fat, 4 g fiber, 345 mg sodium

WHY YOU
SHOULD
CHOOSE

Chicken with Skin

Unless a recipe indicates otherwise, go ahead and buy the chicken breasts with the skin still attached. Eating a chicken breast with the skin on adds more than 20 percent additional calories. But leaving the skin on during cooking—and removing it before serving—helps keep the meat moist without adding extra calories.

Mexican Chopped Salad

Jicama is a crisp, sweet vegetable that resembles a potato in appearance. When shopping for jicama, choose medium-size bulbs (less than two fists together) or smaller, without any bruising.

½ cup chopped fresh cilantro

1 clove garlic

2 tablespoons lime juice

½ teaspoon ground cumin

⅛ teaspoon salt

¼ cup olive oil

6 cups chopped romaine lettuce

3 cups shredded cooked skinless chicken breast

1 can (15 ounces) pinto or kidney beans, rinsed and drained

1 small jicama (about 8 ounces), peeled and chopped

1 cup grape tomatoes, quartered

COMBINE the cilantro, garlic, lime juice, cumin, and salt in a food processor or blender. Pulse until the garlic is chopped. Add the oil in a steady stream, pulsing until emulsified.

ARRANGE the lettuce on a serving plate. Place the chicken, beans, jicama, and tomatoes in piles on the lettuce. Drizzle with the dressing.

TOTAL TIME: 20 minutes **MAKES 4 SERVINGS**

PER SERVING: 386 calories, 30 g protein, 26 g carbohydrates, 18 g total fat, 3 g saturated fat, 12 g fiber, 324 mg sodium

Middle Eastern Chopped Salad

Even those who think they don't like salad will be won over by the fresh flavors and variety of textures in this easy-to-put-together dish.

¼ cup extra-virgin olive oil

2 tablespoons
red wine vinegar

1 garlic clove, minced

½ teaspoon salt

¼ teaspoon ground
black pepper

3 tomatoes, chopped

1 cucumber, peeled, seeded,
and chopped

1 red bell pepper, seeded
and chopped

1 green bell pepper,
seeded and chopped

½ pound chopped cooked
skinless chicken breast

¼ red onion, finely chopped

2 tablespoons chopped
fresh parsley

2 tablespoons crumbled
feta cheese

2 whole wheat pitas
(6" diameter)

WHISK together the oil, vinegar, garlic, salt, and pepper in a small bowl.

COMBINE the tomatoes, cucumber, bell peppers, and chicken in a large bowl. Toss to combine. Add the dressing, onion, parsley, and cheese. Toss again until thoroughly combined.

DIVIDE among 4 bowls. Toast the pitas and cut each into 4 wedges. Serve 2 wedges with each salad.

TOTAL TIME: 25 minutes **MAKES 4 SERVINGS**

PER SERVING: 338 calories, 22 g protein, 22 g carbohydrates, 18 g total fat, 3.5 g saturated fat, 5 g fiber, 514 mg sodium

Mediterranean Grain Salad

Bulgur is boiled, dried, and cracked wheat kernels. For a chewy texture, simply reconstitute it by soaking in liquid. For a fluffy grain, cook it further.

4 cups baby arugula

1 cup cooked bulgur, cooled to room temperature

½ cup (2 ounces) chopped part-skim mozzarella cheese

1 grilled boneless, skinless chicken breast half (about 6 ounces), chopped

1 roasted red bell pepper, chopped

2 tablespoons bottled balsamic vinaigrette

COMBINE the arugula, bulgur, cheese, chicken, bell pepper, and vinaigrette in a large bowl and toss gently until thoroughly combined.

TOTAL TIME: 10 minutes **MAKES 2 SERVINGS**

PER SERVING: 357 calories, 37 g protein, 22 g carbohydrates, 13 g total fat, 5 g saturated fat, 5 g fiber, 382 mg sodium

Grilled Panzanella Salad

Panzanella is a classic Italian salad that's typically made with day-old bread and fresh tomatoes. In this version, all the key ingredients are grilled first to intensify their flavors. A small bit of beef makes it a hearty dinner salad.

1 small eggplant, peeled and coarsely chopped

1 zucchini, coarsely chopped

1 red bell pepper, seeded and coarsely chopped

1 onion, thinly sliced

¾ pound top round sirloin steak

¼ teaspoon salt

¼ teaspoon ground black pepper

4 thick slices 9-grain bread, cut into 1" cubes

1 cup fresh basil leaves

6 cups baby arugula

⅓ cup bottled low-fat balsamic vinaigrette

COAT a vegetable grill basket or broiler-pan rack with cooking spray. Preheat the grill or broiler. Place the eggplant, zucchini, bell pepper, and onion in the grill basket or on the broiler-pan rack. Coat the vegetables with cooking spray. Sprinkle the steak with the salt and black pepper.

GRILL or broil the vegetables, turning occasionally, for 15 minutes, or until browned and tender.

GRILL or broil the steak for 8 minutes, turning once, or until a thermometer inserted in the center registers 145°F for medium-rare, 160°F for medium, or 165°F for well-done. Let stand for 10 minutes.

COAT the bread with cooking spray and add to the grill basket or broiler-pan rack used for the vegetables. Grill or broil for 2 to 3 minutes, turning once, or until browned. Place the vegetables and bread in a large bowl.

ADD the basil, arugula, and vinaigrette to the bowl with the bread and vegetables. Toss to coat. Slice the steak.

DIVIDE the steak and salad among 4 plates and serve immediately.

TOTAL TIME: 50 minutes **MAKES 4 SERVINGS**

PER SERVING: 320 calories, 28 g protein, 39 g carbohydrates, 7 g total fat, 2 g saturated fat, 11 g fiber, 692 mg sodium

Vietnamese Beef Salad

This light and flavorful grilled salad is perfect for hot summer nights. Serve with steamed jasmine rice, if desired.

¼ cup less-sodium soy sauce

¼ cup lime juice

¼ cup water

2 tablespoons sugar

1 tablespoon minced garlic

2 teaspoons chile paste

½ pound flank steak

6 cups mixed greens

1 cup sliced fresh basil

1 cup chopped fresh cilantro

1 large red onion, thinly sliced

2 large seedless cucumbers, cut into thin strips

4 carrots, cut into thin strips

2 tablespoons chopped dry-roasted, unsalted peanuts

WHISK together the soy sauce, lime juice, water, sugar, garlic, and chile paste in a medium bowl. Pour 3 tablespoons of the soy sauce mixture into a resealable plastic bag. Cover and chill the remaining mixture to use as a dressing for the salad. Add the steak to the bag, seal, and turn to coat. Chill for 30 minutes.

COAT a grill rack or broiler-pan rack with cooking spray. Preheat the grill or broiler. Remove the steak from the marinade, discarding the marinade. Grill or broil the steak for 8 to 10 minutes, turning once, or until a thermometer inserted in the center registers 145°F for medium-rare. Let stand for 5 minutes before thinly slicing at an angle, across the grain.

COMBINE the greens, basil, and cilantro in a large bowl and divide evenly among 4 plates. Sprinkle with the onion, cucumbers, and carrots. Top with the steak, drizzle with the reserved dressing, and sprinkle with the peanuts.

TOTAL TIME: 55 minutes **MAKES 4 SERVINGS**

PER SERVING: 252 calories, 18 g protein, 27 g carbohydrates, 8 g total fat, 2 g saturated fat, 5 g fiber, 699 mg sodium

Grilled Steak and Peach Salad

If peaches are out of season, change up this recipe by using fresh pineapple or mango in their place.

1½ tablespoons white wine vinegar

1 tablespoon olive oil

1 tablespoon orange juice

½ teaspoon grated fresh ginger

¼ teaspoon salt

2 large peaches, halved and pitted

1 small sirloin steak (8 ounces), trimmed of excess fat

¼ teaspoon ground black pepper

1 red bell pepper, seeded and cut into thin, short strips

1 bag (5 ounces) fresh baby spinach

3 tablespoons sliced almonds

¼ cup fresh basil leaves, torn

4 slices wheat bread, toasted

HEAT a grill pan coated with cooking spray over medium-high heat.

WHISK together the vinegar, oil, orange juice, ginger, and salt in a medium bowl. Set the dressing aside. Coat the cut surfaces of the peaches with olive oil cooking spray. Season the steak with the black pepper.

PLACE the steak and peaches, cut sides down, on the grill pan. Grill the peaches for 6 minutes, or until soft. Grill the steak for 8 minutes, turning once, or until a thermometer inserted in the center registers 145°F for medium-rare, 160°F for medium, or 165°F for well-done. Let stand for 5 minutes before thinly slicing.

SLICE the peaches into wedges. Add the bell pepper and spinach to the bowl with the dressing and toss to coat. Divide the spinach mixture among 4 plates. Top with the steak and peaches. Sprinkle with the almonds and basil. Serve with the toast.

TOTAL TIME: 20 minutes **MAKES 4 SERVINGS**

PER SERVING: 286 calories, 23 g protein, 30 g carbohydrates, 10 g total fat, 2 g saturated fat, 6 g fiber, 370 mg sodium

Sides

CHAPTER

9

Sautéed Cherry Tomatoes and White Beans

White beans go perfectly with the other Italian flavors in this dish. Cooking the beans for just a couple of minutes helps make them deliciously soft and juicy.

1 teaspoon olive oil

3 scallions, chopped

2 teaspoons thinly sliced fresh sage

3 cups cherry tomatoes, halved

1 cup canned no-salt-added white beans, rinsed and drained

⅛ teaspoon salt

⅛ teaspoon ground black pepper

HEAT the oil in a nonstick skillet over medium heat. Add the scallions and cook, stirring frequently, for 1 minute, or until softened. Stir in the sage.

ADD the tomatoes and beans. Cook, stirring frequently, for 2 minutes, or until the tomatoes soften. Stir in the salt and pepper.

TOTAL TIME: 20 minutes **MAKES 4 SERVINGS**

PER SERVING: 90 calories, 5 g protein, 15 g carbohydrates, 2 g total fat, 0 g saturated fat, 7 g fiber, 120 mg sodium

Spinach Pasta May Be a Veggie Impostor

Not every product that boasts "spinach" on the label is even remotely like a serving of the real thing. Nonetheless, manufacturers hope that spinach's health halo will lead you to buy their pasta. But read labels carefully before you do. Put a product back if the Nutrition Facts panel doesn't boast 25 percent of your vitamin A and 2 grams of fiber. And remember the basic rule: If it doesn't look like a vegetable, it probably isn't

Roasted Broccoli with Orange

For those who dislike the texture of broccoli when it is steamed or boiled, roasting is the perfect alternative. This dry-heat method helps the florets hold a lot of flavor in between their buds.

1 pound broccoli, tops cut into florets and stems peeled, quartered lengthwise, and cut into 2" lengths

2 tablespoons olive oil

2 cloves garlic, thinly sliced

2 teaspoons grated orange peel (optional)

½ teaspoon salt

2 tablespoons orange juice

Ground black pepper

PREHEAT the oven to 425°F. Line a rimmed baking sheet with parchment paper.

COMBINE the broccoli, oil, garlic, orange peel (if using), and salt on the baking sheet and toss to coat. Spread in a single layer and roast for 20 minutes, or until the edges are brown and the stems are tender.

TOSS with the orange juice and season to taste with the pepper.

TOTAL TIME: 25 minutes **MAKES 4 SERVINGS**

PER SERVING: 104 calories, 3 g protein, 4 g carbohydrates, 7 g total fat, 1 g saturated fat, 3 g fiber, 329 mg sodium

Asparagus and Sugar Snap Toss

Tasty, high in fiber, low in calories, and quick to prepare—what other reason do you need to throw together this side dish for dinner tonight?

1½ teaspoons olive oil

1½ pounds asparagus, trimmed and cut into 1" pieces

1 tablespoon water

½ pound sugar snap peas, ends trimmed and strings removed

3 scallions, sliced

1½ teaspoons reduced-sodium soy sauce

1½ teaspoons honey

½ teaspoon salt

¼ teaspoon ground black pepper

HEAT the oil in a large skillet with a lid over medium heat. Add the asparagus and water. Cover and steam for 5 minutes.

ADD the peas, scallions, soy sauce, and honey. Cover and cook for 5 minutes, or until the vegetables are tender.

SEASON with the salt and pepper. Serve warm or at room temperature.

TOTAL TIME: 20 minutes **MAKES 8 SERVINGS**

PER SERVING: 34 calories, 2 g protein, 5 g carbohydrates, 1 g total fat, 0 g saturated fat, 2 g fiber, 36 mg sodium

Twice-Baked Curried Potatoes

Here's a novel spin on twice-baked potatoes. Instead of being loaded down with cheese and sour cream, these snappy spuds burst with flavorful spices and sweet peas.

2 large baking potatoes, scrubbed

2½ teaspoons olive oil, divided

1 onion, finely chopped

1 tablespoon finely chopped fresh ginger

2 teaspoons curry powder

1 cup vegetable broth

1 cup frozen green peas, thawed

¼ cup chopped fresh cilantro

2 tablespoons chutney

PREHEAT the oven to 400°F.

COAT the potatoes with ½ teaspoon of the oil. Poke the skins a few times with the tines of a fork. Place on a microwaveable plate and microwave on high power for 8 minutes, or until soft. Let the potatoes cool slightly, then cut in half lengthwise. Scoop out the flesh into a medium bowl, leaving enough potato attached to the skin to form a sturdy shell. Set the shells aside.

MEANWHILE, heat the remaining 2 teaspoons oil in a large nonstick skillet over medium heat. Add the onion and ginger and cook, stirring occasionally, for 5 minutes, or until the onion softens. Add the curry powder and cook for 1 minute longer, or until fragrant.

ADD the onion mixture to the potato pulp and mash to combine. Add the broth and continue mashing until smooth. Stir in the peas, cilantro, and chutney.

FILL the reserved shells with the potato mixture. Place on a small baking sheet and bake for 12 minutes, or until warmed through.

TOTAL TIME: 35 minutes **MAKES 4 SERVINGS**

PER SERVING: 240 calories, 6 g protein, 47 g carbohydrates, 3 g total fat, 0.5 g saturated fat, 7 g fiber, 235 mg sodium

Mashed Sweet Potatoes with Apple Juice

Even if you're trying to trim the fat from your diet, don't cut the butter out of this recipe. Research shows that eating just a small amount of fat significantly increases our ability to absorb the beta-carotene from sweet potatoes.

4 sweet potatoes, peeled and cut into large chunks

⅔ cup apple juice

1 tablespoon butter

½ teaspoon salt

¼ teaspoon ground nutmeg

Generous pinch of ground black pepper

BRING the potatoes and juice to a boil in a medium saucepan. Reduce the heat, cover, and simmer, stirring occasionally, for 25 minutes, or until the potatoes are soft enough to mash.

COMBINE the potatoes, juice, butter, salt, nutmeg, and pepper in a food processor. Puree until smooth. Taste and, if necessary, adjust the seasonings before serving.

TOTAL TIME: 40 minutes **MAKES 4 SERVINGS**

PER SERVING: 180 calories, 3 g protein, 36 g carbohydrates, 3 g total fat, 2 g saturated fat, 5 g fiber, 360 mg sodium

Bay Roasted New Potatoes

Aromatic bay leaves subtly infuse this dish for a brand-new twist on plain old potatoes. Feel free to substitute your favorite herb—rosemary and thyme work well, too.

2 **pounds new potatoes (such as fingerling), less than 3" in diameter, halved**

¼ **cup olive oil**

6 **dried bay leaves**

1 **teaspoon salt**

1 **teaspoon paprika**

¼ **teaspoon ground black pepper**

Pinch of ground red pepper

2 **tablespoons butter**

PREHEAT the oven to 425°F.

COMBINE the potatoes, oil, bay leaves, salt, paprika, black pepper, and red pepper in a medium bowl. Toss thoroughly to coat.

SPREAD the potato mixture on a rimmed baking sheet. Roast for 30 to 40 minutes, stirring and turning with a spatula halfway through the cooking time, or until the potatoes are tender.

RETURN the potatoes to the bowl and toss with the butter. Remove and discard the bay leaves.

TOTAL TIME: 45 minutes **MAKES 6 SERVINGS**

PER SERVING: 232 calories, 3 g protein, 27 g carbohydrates, 13 g total fat, 4 g saturated fat, 4 g fiber, 521 mg sodium

Mediterranean Couscous

Israeli couscous is a type of toasted pasta shaped like little balls that was originally invented as a wheat-based alternative to rice. If gluten sensitivity is a concern, substitute your favorite long-grain rice in this dish.

1 zucchini, chopped

2 tablespoons + ½ teaspoon olive oil

¼ teaspoon salt

¼ cup golden raisins

1 cup Israeli couscous

¼ cup pine nuts

1 can (15 ounces) chickpeas, rinsed and drained

½ small onion, thinly sliced

¼ cup chopped fresh parsley

2 teaspoons cider vinegar or lemon juice

PREHEAT the oven to 425°F. Line a rimmed baking sheet with parchment paper.

COMBINE the zucchini, ½ teaspoon of the oil, and salt on the baking sheet and toss to coat. Spread in a single layer and roast for 15 minutes, or until the edges begin to turn brown.

MEANWHILE, soak the raisins in enough hot water to cover in a small bowl for at least 10 minutes. Drain and place in a large bowl.

BRING 1 quart water to a boil in a large saucepan. Add the couscous and cook for 8 minutes, or just until the couscous is soft. Drain and add to the bowl with the raisins.

TOAST the pine nuts in a small dry skillet over medium-high heat for 5 minutes, or until fragrant.

ADD the pine nuts, chickpeas, onion, parsley, and zucchini to the couscous mixture. Toss to combine. Drizzle with the vinegar or lemon juice and remaining 2 tablespoons oil.

TOTAL TIME: 35 minutes **MAKES 6 SERVINGS**

PER SERVING: 263 calories, 8 g protein, 38 g carbohydrates, 10 g total fat, 1 g saturated fat, 4 g fiber, 274 mg sodium

Creamy Polenta

Polenta cooks quickly and can form clumps when the grain is added to the hot cooking liquid. Mixing it with a small amount of water beforehand ensures this will not happen.

¾ cup reduced-sodium chicken broth

¾ cup 1% milk

½ cup water

½ cup polenta

BRING the broth and milk to a boil in a medium saucepan.

COMBINE the water and polenta in a small bowl. Pour the polenta mixture into the broth mixture and stir well.

REDUCE the heat so that the polenta is barely bubbling. Cook, stirring constantly, for 10 to 15 minutes, or until the polenta is thick, tender, and no longer grainy.

TOTAL TIME: 20 minutes **MAKES 2 SERVINGS**

PER SERVING: 162 calories, 6 g protein, 29 g carbohydrates, 2 g total fat, 1 g saturated fat, 5 g fiber, 80 mg sodium

Greek-Style Brown Rice

Brown rice supplies more vitamins, minerals, protein, and fiber than white rice, and this cooking method ensures perfect results. Make sure to use long-grain brown rice if you prefer rice that is slightly more tender and fluffy.

1 box (10 ounces) frozen chopped spinach, thawed and drained

¾ cup brown rice

3 plum tomatoes, cored, seeded, and chopped

1 onion, chopped

1 clove garlic, minced

½ teaspoon salt

1½ cups boiling water

½ cup crumbled reduced-fat feta cheese

PREHEAT the oven to 375°F.

STIR together the spinach, rice, tomatoes, onion, garlic, and salt in a 1½-quart baking dish with a lid. Stir in the boiling water. Cover and bake for 1 hour, or until all the liquid is absorbed and the rice is tender. Sprinkle with the cheese.

TOTAL TIME: 1 hour 10 minutes **MAKES 4 SERVINGS**

PER SERVING: 204 calories, 10 g protein, 35 g carbohydrates, 4 g total fat, 2 g saturated fat, 5 g fiber, 587 mg sodium

Snack Food Nation

As if we didn't already have enough snack opportunities, chain restaurants are beefing up their so-called snack menus, which are designed to draw in customers during off-hours. Since 2007, the number of restaurant items listed as "snacks," "snackable," or "snackers" has grown by 170 percent, including items such as KFC's Snacker with a crispy chicken strip, McDonald's Angus Mushroom Swiss Snack Wrap, and the Cheese and Tomato Deep Dish Pizza from the Snack Hours Menu at Uno Chicago Grill—weighing in at 290, 430, and 830 calories, respectively.

Butternut Squash Risotto

Arborio rice creates its own creamy sauce, so leftover risotto freezes very well. If it separates when thawed, puree one-third in a blender and stir in when reheating.

1 large butternut squash

5 cups reduced-sodium chicken broth

1 tablespoon olive oil

3 cloves garlic, minced

2 cups arborio rice

¼ cup chopped fresh parsley

¼ cup grated Parmesan cheese + additional for garnish (optional)

¼ teaspoon salt

¼ teaspoon ground black pepper

PIERCE the squash several times with a sharp knife. Place it on a paper towel in the microwave oven. Microwave on high power for 15 minutes. Halve the squash lengthwise. Remove and discard the seeds. Place the halves back on the paper towel and microwave for 5 minutes longer, or until tender. Let cool slightly, then scoop the flesh into a bowl. Discard the shells and cut the flesh into small chunks.

PLACE the broth in a medium saucepan and bring to a simmer over medium-high heat. Reduce the heat to low and keep the broth warm.

HEAT a Dutch oven coated with cooking spray over medium-high heat. Add the oil and garlic. Cook, stirring occasionally, for 1 minute. Add the rice. Cook, stirring occasionally, for 5 minutes.

ADD the squash and ½ cup of the broth. Cook, stirring constantly, until the liquid completely evaporates. Add ½ cup of the remaining broth. Cook, stirring occasionally, until the liquid is absorbed.

CONTINUE to add the broth, ½ cup at a time, stirring after each addition until the liquid is absorbed. Cook for a total of 25 minutes, or until the rice is creamy and tender. Stir in the parsley, ¼ cup of the cheese, salt, and pepper. Garnish with additional cheese, if desired.

TOTAL TIME: 1 hour **MAKES 6 SERVINGS**

PER SERVING: 391 calories, 12 g protein, 72 g carbohydrates, 6 g total fat, 2 g saturated fat, 4 g fiber, 440 mg sodium

Quinoa Pilaf

Quinoa is a grain from South America that packs a low-fat, high-protein punch. It's a great grain to incorporate into your diet if you're looking for a lean protein alternative to meat.

2 tablespoons pine nuts

1 cup quinoa

½ tablespoon olive oil

½ yellow onion, finely chopped

1 carrot, finely chopped

3 cups low-sodium chicken broth or water

¼ cup golden raisins

½ cup chopped fresh parsley

TOAST the pine nuts in a small dry skillet over medium-high heat for 5 minutes, or until fragrant. Place on a small plate and set aside.

PLACE the quinoa in a large bowl and rinse several times in cold water, changing the water each time. Drain thoroughly.

HEAT the oil in a medium saucepan over medium heat. Cook the onion and carrot for 5 minutes, or until softened. Add the quinoa and cook, stirring occasionally, for 3 minutes, or until the quinoa is lightly toasted and gives off a nutty aroma. Add the broth or water and bring to a simmer. Reduce the heat to low, cover, and simmer for 20 minutes, or until the liquid is completely absorbed.

TRANSFER the quinoa to a large bowl and fluff with a fork. Stir in the pine nuts, raisins, and parsley.

TOTAL TIME: 40 minutes **MAKES 4 SERVINGS**

PER SERVING: 277 calories, 11 g protein, 41 g carbohydrates, 8 g total fat, 1 g saturated fat, 5 g fiber, 113 mg sodium

Toasted Rice Pilaf

Toasting the rice and cumin before adding the broth brings out the grain's naturally nutty flavor.

1 cup long-grain white rice, such as basmati

2 teaspoons olive oil

1 teaspoon minced garlic

½ teaspoon ground cumin

2 cups reduced-sodium chicken broth

¼ teaspoon salt

¼ cup finely chopped fresh parsley

HEAT a nonstick skillet over medium-high heat. Add the rice, oil, garlic, and cumin. Cook, stirring constantly, for 3 to 5 minutes, or until fragrant.

ADD the broth and salt. Bring to a boil. Reduce the heat to low, cover, and cook for 20 minutes, or until the rice is tender. Sprinkle with the parsley.

TOTAL TIME: 30 minutes **MAKES 4 SERVINGS**

PER SERVING: 235 calories, 7 g protein, 42 g carbohydrates, 4 g total fat, 1 g saturated fat, 1 g fiber, 322 mg sodium

Middle Eastern Rice Salad

This is a great salad to make if you have just a few cups of leftover brown rice in the fridge. Add the trimmed ends and leaves of the celery to the pan with the lentils for a boost of flavor (remove and discard after cooking). If you have fresh mint on hand, chop some leaves to add to the salad. Serve at room temperature or chilled.

1 cup brown lentils

3 tablespoons fresh lemon juice

2 teaspoons olive oil

1 teaspoon grated lemon peel

½ teaspoon smoked paprika

¼ teaspoon salt

⅛ teaspoon ground red pepper

1½ cups cooked brown rice

2 carrots, shredded

2 ribs celery, chopped

2 tomatoes, seeded and chopped

1 small red onion, chopped

¾ cup chopped fresh parsley

BRING 1 quart water to a boil in a large saucepan. Add the lentils and reduce the heat to a simmer. Cook for 15 minutes, or just until tender. Drain well and cool.

MEANWHILE, whisk together the lemon juice, oil, lemon peel, paprika, salt, and red pepper in a large bowl.

ADD the rice, carrots, celery, tomatoes, onion, parsley, and cooled lentils. Stir to combine.

TOTAL TIME: 25 minutes **MAKES 4 SERVINGS**

PER SERVING: 305 calories, 16 g protein, 54 g carbohydrates, 4 g total fat, 1 g saturated fat, 15 g fiber, 204 mg sodium

Vegetarian

CHAPTER
10

Goat Cheese–Asparagus Frittata

Perfect for breakfast, brunch, or dinner, this savory egg dish is a fast and easy way to enjoy asparagus, a vegetable that provides a wide variety of antioxidant nutrients, including vitamin C, beta-carotene, vitamin E, and the minerals zinc, manganese, and selenium.

1 teaspoon olive oil

1 pound asparagus, trimmed and cut into 1" pieces (slice lengthwise first if spears are thick)

¼ teaspoon salt

6 eggs

4 ounces soft goat cheese, sliced

PREHEAT the broiler.

HEAT the oil in a medium ovenproof nonstick skillet over medium heat. Add the asparagus and cook, covered, for 2 to 3 minutes, or until the asparagus begins to soften. Sprinkle with the salt.

BEAT the eggs in a large bowl. Add the eggs to the skillet and cook for 3 minutes to set the bottom. Reduce the heat to medium-low and cook for 3 to 5 minutes, lifting the edges occasionally and tilting the pan so the uncooked eggs flow to the bottom. When the eggs have set around the edges, arrange the goat cheese on top of the frittata.

BROIL 5" from the heat for 2 to 3 minutes, or until the frittata is lightly browned and the center is set. Serve warm or at room temperature.

TOTAL TIME: 25 minutes **MAKES 4 SERVINGS**

PER SERVING: 216 calories, 17 g protein, 5 g carbohydrates, 15 g total fat, 7 g saturated fat, 2 g fiber, 357 mg sodium

Spinach-Tomato Frittata

Any egg-based main dish makes an affordable alternative to pricier meat-based ones. As an added bonus, frozen or fresh spinach turns this frittata into a nutrient-packed dish that is ready in 15 minutes or less.

2 tablespoons olive oil, divided

2 scallions, thinly sliced

1 package (10 ounces) frozen chopped spinach, thawed and squeezed dry

3 eggs

5 egg whites

1 cup grape or cherry tomatoes

4 slices (1 ounce each) part-skim mozzarella cheese

4 slices whole grain bread, toasted

PREHEAT the broiler.

HEAT 1 tablespoon of the oil in a large ovenproof nonstick skillet over medium heat. Cook the scallions, stirring occasionally, for 1 minute, or until softened.

TRANSFER the scallions to a large bowl. Add the spinach, eggs, and egg whites. Beat with a fork until well blended.

HEAT the remaining 1 tablespoon oil in the same skillet over medium heat. Pour the egg mixture into the skillet and scatter the tomatoes on top. Cover and cook for 4 minutes, or until the eggs are set around the edges. Uncover.

BROIL 5" from the heat for 4 minutes, or until the frittata is lightly browned and the center is set. Remove from the oven and top with the cheese. Cover and let stand for 1 minute to let the cheese melt. Cut into 4 wedges and serve each with 1 slice of toast.

TOTAL TIME: 15 minutes **MAKES 4 SERVINGS**

PER SERVING: 317 calories, 23 g protein, 18 g carbohydrates, 18 g total fat, 5 g saturated fat, 5 g fiber, 434 mg sodium

Everyday Soufflé

To prevent your soufflé from falling, keep the oven door shut until it's at least 75 percent cooked. Also, serve it immediately.

1 tablespoon dried bread crumbs

1 pound broccoli, cut into florets

3 egg yolks

1½ cups fat-free milk

⅓ cup all-purpose flour

¾ teaspoon mustard powder

1 clove garlic, minced

½ cup grated Romano cheese

6 egg whites

⅛ teaspoon cream of tartar

PREHEAT the oven to 375°F. Coat a 2-quart soufflé dish with cooking spray. Add the bread crumbs and shake to coat.

PLACE a steamer basket in a large pot with 2" of water. Bring to a boil over high heat. Place the broccoli in the basket and steam for 8 minutes, or until very tender. Drain and rinse under cold running water. Place on a clean kitchen towel to dry. Finely chop and place in a large bowl.

WHISK together the egg yolks in a small bowl and set aside. Whisk together the milk, flour, mustard, and garlic in a medium saucepan. Bring to a boil over medium heat. Reduce the heat and simmer, stirring constantly, for 3 minutes, or until slightly thickened. Remove from the heat. Whisk about ½ cup of the milk mixture into the egg yolks. Whisk the egg yolk mixture into the saucepan. Cook for 2 minutes, or until thick. Pour into the bowl with the broccoli and stir in the cheese.

BEAT the egg whites and cream of tartar in a large mixing bowl with an electric mixer on high speed until stiff, glossy peaks form, occasionally scraping down the sides of the bowl with a rubber spatula.

STIR about one-third of the whites into the broccoli mixture. Fold in the remaining whites. Pour into the soufflé dish. Bake for 30 to 40 minutes, or until puffed and golden.

TOTAL TIME: 1 hour 15 minutes MAKES 4 SERVINGS

PER SERVING: 237 calories, 20 g protein, 23 g carbohydrates, 8 g total fat, 4 g saturated fat, 5 g fiber, 407 mg sodium

Arugula Pesto Patties

Leftover brown rice works well for this dish, but if you do not have any, cook ¾ cup brown rice (either regular or quick-cooking) to yield 2 cups.

1 **package (14 ounces) extra-firm tofu**

4 **cups (4 ounces) baby arugula**

⅓ **cup chopped walnuts**

2 **cloves garlic, peeled and halved**

1 **tablespoon olive oil**

¾ **teaspoon salt, divided**

⅛ **teaspoon ground black pepper**

2 **cups cooked brown rice**

1 **small onion, chopped and divided**

1 **tablespoon chopped fresh oregano**

1 **pound green beans**

4 **cups sliced red cabbage**

PLACE the tofu in a colander in the sink. Top with a flat plate weighted down with a heavy can of vegetables. Let stand for 15 minutes to drain.

PREHEAT the oven to 400°F. Coat a large rimmed baking sheet with cooking spray.

PROCESS the arugula, walnuts, garlic, oil, ⅛ teaspoon of the salt, and pepper in a food processor for 1 minute, or until smooth. Transfer the pesto to a small bowl and set aside.

PROCESS the tofu in the food processor for 1 minute, or until chopped. Add the rice, half of the onion, oregano, ½ teaspoon of the salt, and 2 tablespoons of the arugula pesto. Process for 1 minute. Form the mixture into 8 patties and set aside.

COMBINE the green beans, cabbage, and remaining onion on the rimmed baking sheet. Coat with cooking spray and sprinkle with the remaining ⅛ teaspoon salt. Roast for 10 minutes, or until the vegetables are lightly browned.

MEANWHILE, heat a large nonstick skillet coated with cooking spray over medium-high heat. Cook the patties for 8 minutes, turning once, or until browned.

ARRANGE 2 patties on each of 4 plates, top with the arugula pesto, and serve with the vegetables on the side.

TOTAL TIME: 45 minutes **MAKES 4 SERVINGS**

PER SERVING: 398 calories, 21 g protein, 44 g carbohydrates, 19 g total fat, 2.5 g saturated fat, 10 g fiber, 485 mg sodium

Heavenly Hash

Most food historians agree that the name for this popular dish comes from the French word *hachis*, derived from *hacher*, which means "to chop." As for the heavenly reference, one bite and you'll know how that became part of the recipe title, too.

1 tablespoon olive oil

3 large potatoes, chopped

½ teaspoon salt

¼ teaspoon ground black pepper

1 small yellow onion, chopped

½ red bell pepper, seeded and chopped

½ cup frozen yellow corn, thawed

2 tablespoons chopped fresh parsley

HEAT the oil in a large nonstick skillet over medium-high heat. Add the potatoes, salt, and black pepper and cook, stirring frequently, for 10 to 12 minutes, or until the edges start to brown.

ADD the onion and bell pepper and cook for 5 minutes, or until the onion is soft and the potatoes are browned. Stir in the corn and parsley. Remove from the heat and serve.

TOTAL TIME: 30 minutes   **MAKES 4 SERVINGS**

PER SERVING: 272 calories, 7 g protein, 55 g carbohydrates, 4 g total fat, 0.5 g saturated fat, 7 g fiber, 310 mg sodium

Pesto Gnocchi with Green Beans and Tomatoes

The Italian potato dumplings better known as gnocchi are easy to find in the freezer case or vacuum-packed on a shelf near the pasta options.

1 tablespoon olive oil

1 pound green beans

1 pint cherry tomatoes

1 package (16 ounces) potato gnocchi

½ cup prepared pesto

1 cup bite-size cubes fresh mozzarella cheese

4 teaspoons freshly grated Parmesan cheese

HEAT the oil in a large nonstick skillet over medium heat. Add the green beans and cook for 3 minutes. Add the tomatoes and cook for 3 minutes, or until the green beans are tender-crisp and the tomatoes are browned on the outside. Remove from the heat.

MEANWHILE, bring a large pot of salted water to a boil. Cook the gnocchi for 4 to 5 minutes, or until they float to the surface. Drain.

ADD the gnocchi to the skillet with the green beans and tomatoes. Stir in the pesto and mozzarella. Divide among 4 warm plates or bowls and top each with 1 teaspoon of the grated Parmesan.

TOTAL TIME: 25 minutes **MAKES 4 SERVINGS**

PER SERVING: 470 calories, 15 g protein, 32 g carbohydrates, 33 g total fat, 13 g saturated fat, 6 g fiber, 395 mg sodium

Brown Rice with Squash and Chickpeas

Although you can find winter squash throughout much of the year, they're sweetest just after the fall harvest. Choose heavy, firm, stem-on squash without soft spots. Store them someplace cool and dry, and they'll keep for several weeks. Or buy this veggie peeled and cubed to save time and effort.

- **4 teaspoons olive oil, divided**
- **1 onion, halved and thinly sliced**
- **3 large cloves garlic, minced and divided**
- **1 tablespoon grated fresh ginger**
- **2½ cups water**
- **1 cup brown rice**
- **½ cup lentils**
- **¾ teaspoon salt, divided**
- **1 can (15 ounces) chickpeas, rinsed and drained**
- **2 cups chopped butternut squash**
- **2 bunches broccoli rabe, trimmed and cut into 2" pieces**
- **½ teaspoon red-pepper flakes**

HEAT 2 teaspoons of the oil in a large, deep skillet over medium heat. Add the onion. Cook, stirring frequently, for 8 minutes, or until lightly browned.

ADD half of the garlic and the ginger. Cook for 1 minute, stirring constantly. Add the water, rice, lentils, and ½ teaspoon of the salt. Bring to a boil. Cover, reduce the heat, and simmer for 30 minutes. Stir in the chickpeas and squash. Cover and cook for 15 to 20 minutes, or until the rice is tender.

MEANWHILE, bring a large pot of water to a boil. Stir in the broccoli rabe and cook for 2 minutes. Drain, reserving ¼ cup of the cooking liquid. In the same pot, heat the remaining 2 teaspoons oil over low heat. Add the red-pepper flakes and remaining garlic. Cook, stirring constantly, for 1 minute, or until the garlic is sizzling but not brown. Add the broccoli rabe and remaining ¼ teaspoon salt. Cook, stirring occasionally, for 10 to 12 minutes, or until tender, adding the reserved cooking liquid if necessary.

SERVE the rice mixture topped with the broccoli rabe.

TOTAL TIME: 1 hour 25 minutes **MAKES 6 SERVINGS**

PER SERVING: 333 calories, 16 g protein, 58 g carbohydrates, 5 g total fat, 1 g saturated fat, 10 g fiber, 421 mg sodium

Evening Strata

Simply assemble this dish in the morning, cover, and refrigerate until you get home from work. Then pop it in the oven for a refreshingly easy weeknight meal.

6 **eggs**

2 **cups 2% milk**

1 **baguette (8 ounces)**

2 **teaspoons olive oil**

½ **red bell pepper, seeded and finely chopped**

½ **yellow or orange bell pepper, seeded and finely chopped**

½ **red onion, finely chopped**

1 **cup shredded reduced-fat Cheddar cheese**

PREHEAT the oven to 350°F. Coat an 8" × 8" baking dish with cooking spray.

WHISK together the eggs and milk in a large bowl. Set aside.

SLICE the baguette into ½"-thick slices and arrange half of the bread in the baking dish. Pour half of the egg mixture over the bread and let soak.

MEANWHILE, heat the oil in a medium nonstick skillet over medium-high heat. Cook the peppers and onion for 5 minutes, or until the vegetables soften.

SCATTER half of the vegetables over the bread in the baking dish. Top with the remaining bread, vegetables, and egg mixture. Scatter the cheese on top.

BAKE for 35 minutes, or until the strata is set. Place under the broiler for 2 to 3 minutes if a brown top is desired. Let stand for 5 minutes before serving.

TOTAL TIME: 1 hour **MAKES 4 SERVINGS**

PER SERVING: 465 calories, 29 g protein, 49 g carbohydrates, 18 g total fat, 8 g saturated fat, 3 g fiber, 769 mg sodium

Greek-Style Strata

What makes this strata Greek is the feta cheese and the combination of mint and lemon. Instead of the sandwich bread used in most stratas, the bread here is pita, so named for the Greek word for pie, cake, or bread.

3 whole wheat pitas
(8" diameter),
cut into sixths

1 cup 1% cottage cheese

1 cup 1% milk

2 tablespoons
all-purpose flour

3 eggs

2 egg whites

3 ounces feta cheese,
crumbled

4 scallions, thinly sliced

½ cup frozen green peas

½ cup snipped fresh dill

¼ cup chopped fresh mint

1 teaspoon grated
lemon peel

¼ teaspoon ground
black pepper

⅛ teaspoon salt

1 tomato, thinly sliced

PREHEAT the oven to 350°F. Toast the pita wedges on a baking sheet in the oven for 5 minutes, or until lightly crisp.

MEANWHILE, combine the cottage cheese, milk, and flour in a food processor and process for 1 minute, or until smooth. Transfer to a medium bowl and stir in the eggs, egg whites, feta, scallions, peas, dill, mint, lemon peel, pepper, and salt.

ARRANGE the pita wedges in an 11" × 7" baking dish and pour the egg mixture over the top. Let stand at room temperature for 10 minutes.

ARRANGE the tomato slices over the top. Bake for 35 minutes, or until the custard is just set.

TOTAL TIME: 1 hour **MAKES 4 SERVINGS**

PER SERVING: 314 calories, 24 g protein, 33 g carbohydrates, 11 g total fat, 5 g saturated fat, 4 g fiber, 351 mg sodium

WHY YOU
SHOULD
CHOOSE

Eggs for a budget-friendly menu

Eggs are among the least expensive and fastest-cooking sources of protein. All the fat, but also most of the nutrients, are in the yolk.

Rustic Tomato Pizza

If you have access to a variety of heirloom tomatoes, by all means use them in this recipe. The more, the merrier!

1 teaspoon sugar

1 package active dry yeast

1 cup warm water (105°–115°F)

3½ cups all-purpose flour, divided

1 teaspoon salt

1 tablespoon olive oil

2 teaspoons yellow cornmeal

1 cup (4 ounces) shredded part-skim mozzarella cheese

2 heirloom tomatoes, sliced

¼ cup small fresh basil leaves

1 cup (4 ounces) shredded smoked provolone cheese

DISSOLVE the sugar and yeast in the water in a large bowl. Let stand for 5 minutes.

COMBINE 3¼ cups of the flour and the salt in a food processor or bowl of an electric mixer fitted with a dough hook. Add the yeast mixture and oil through the feed tube. Process just until the dough comes together (dough will be slightly sticky).

TURN the dough out onto a lightly floured surface. Knead until smooth and elastic (4 to 7 minutes). Add the remaining flour, 1 tablespoon at a time, if the dough sticks to your hands.

PLACE the dough in a large bowl coated with cooking spray, and turn the dough to coat with the cooking spray. Cover and let rise in a warm place (85°F), free from drafts, for 1 hour.

PUNCH the dough down. Cover and let stand for 5 minutes. Line a baking sheet with parchment paper and sprinkle with the cornmeal. Roll the dough into a 12" circle on a floured surface. Place the dough on the baking sheet. Crimp the edges of the dough with your fingers to form a rim. Let rise for 10 minutes.

PREHEAT the oven to 475°F.

SPRINKLE the mozzarella evenly over the dough and arrange the tomato slices evenly on top. Sprinkle with the basil and provolone. Bake for 15 minutes, or until the crust is lightly browned.

TOTAL TIME: 1 hour 45 minutes **MAKES 8 SERVINGS**

PER SERVING: 320 calories, 14 g protein, 46 g carbohydrates, 9 g total fat, 4 g saturated fat, 2 g fiber, 495 mg sodium

Classic Veggie Pizzas

Look for prepared pizza dough in the refrigerated case near the butter and biscuits. If fresh dough isn't available, check the frozen foods section.

1 tablespoon olive oil

8 ounces prepared pizza dough

1 cup canned crushed tomatoes or tomato sauce

1 teaspoon dried oregano

1 teaspoon sugar

½ teaspoon garlic powder

1 small zucchini, thinly sliced

1 cup small broccoli florets

¼ cup sliced red onion

½ cup (2 ounces) shredded part-skim mozzarella cheese

2 tablespoons grated Parmesan cheese

Red-pepper flakes (optional)

PREHEAT the oven to 400°F. Coat a large rimmed baking sheet with the oil.

DIVIDE the dough into 4 equal portions on a lightly floured surface. Working with one at a time, gently stretch each piece into a long rectangle shape. Arrange the rectangles on the baking sheet.

COMBINE the crushed tomatoes or tomato sauce, oregano, sugar, and garlic powder in a small bowl. Spread ¼ cup sauce on each pizza and top with equal portions of the zucchini, broccoli, and onion. Top with equal portions of the mozzarella.

BAKE for 12 to 15 minutes, or until the edges are crisp and the top is beginning to brown. Remove from the oven and sprinkle with the Parmesan and red-pepper flakes, if desired.

TOTAL TIME: 30 minutes **MAKES 4**

PER PIZZA: 276 calories, 11 g protein, 39 g carbohydrates, 9 g total fat, 3 g saturated fat, 3 g fiber, 615 mg sodium

Rotini with Escarole and Cannellini

Rotini pasta has a distinctive corkscrew shape that makes it ideal for holding onto chunky veggie combos like the beans and escarole in this particular mix.

8 ounces tricolor rotini pasta

2 tablespoons olive oil

1 onion, chopped

1 carrot, chopped

4 cloves garlic, minced

1 teaspoon Italian seasoning

¼ teaspoon salt

8 cups chopped escarole

½ cup low-sodium vegetable broth

1 can (19 ounces) cannellini beans, rinsed and drained

PREPARE the pasta according to the package directions.

MEANWHILE, heat the oil in a large saucepan over medium heat. Add the onion, carrot, garlic, seasoning, and salt. Cook, stirring occasionally, for 5 minutes, or until the vegetables are tender.

INCREASE the heat to high. Add the escarole and broth. Cook, stirring occasionally, for 2 minutes, or until the escarole wilts. Add the beans and cook, stirring occasionally, for 2 minutes, or until heated through.

PLACE the pasta in a serving bowl and top with the escarole mixture.

TOTAL TIME: 20 minutes **MAKES 4 SERVINGS**

PER SERVING: 384 calories, 15 g protein, 65 g carbohydrates, 8 g total fat, 1 g saturated fat, 10 g fiber, 447 mg sodium

Shells with Cauliflower and Peas

What goes with pasta even better than peas and carrots? Cauliflower! Plus it offers similar nutritional benefits as broccoli, its cruciferous cousin.

¼ cup walnut pieces

8 ounces whole wheat or regular pasta shells

½ head cauliflower (about 1 pound), cut into small florets

1 large carrot, thinly sliced

1 cup frozen green peas

¼ cup olive oil

¼ cup chopped fresh parsley

1 clove garlic, minced

½ teaspoon salt

¼ teaspoon ground black pepper

¼ cup grated Parmesan cheese

TOAST the walnuts in a small dry skillet over medium-high heat, tossing frequently for 5 minutes, until fragrant. Place on a plate and set aside.

PREPARE the pasta according to the package directions. Add the cauliflower and carrot to the pot during the last 5 minutes of cooking time. Add the peas for the final 2 minutes of cooking time.

LADLE ½ cup of the cooking liquid into a small bowl and set aside. Drain the pasta and vegetables. Immediately return the pasta and vegetables to the pot and add the oil, parsley, garlic, salt, pepper, and reserved cooking liquid. Stir to blend.

SERVE hot, sprinkled with the toasted walnuts and cheese.

TOTAL TIME: 20 minutes **MAKES 4 SERVINGS**

PER SERVING: 464 calories, 14 g protein, 54 g carbohydrates, 22 g total fat, 3 g saturated fat, 9 g fiber, 450 mg sodium

Basic Supper Pasta

Here's a no-nonsense red sauce that would make an Italian nonna proud. Plus, it doubles easily if you want to feed a crowd. We've added cauliflower and butternut squash for an added fiber boost, but toss in other veggies if you prefer.

1 teaspoon olive oil

2 cloves garlic, pressed

1 can (28 ounces) no-salt-added diced tomatoes

½ cup water

½ cup dry red wine or vegetable broth

3 tablespoons tomato paste

1 teaspoon sugar (optional)

½ teaspoon dried oregano

¼ teaspoon salt

⅛ teaspoon ground black pepper

9 ounces linguine

1 cup chopped cauliflower florets

1 cup peeled, chopped butternut squash

2 tablespoons grated Parmesan cheese

HEAT the oil in a Dutch oven over medium-high heat. Add the garlic and cook for 30 seconds, or until fragrant. Reduce the heat to low and add the tomatoes (with juice), water, wine or broth, and tomato paste. Cover and cook for 5 to 7 minutes, stirring occasionally.

ADD the sugar (if using), oregano, salt, and pepper. Simmer, stirring occasionally, for 25 minutes, or until the sauce is thick.

MEANWHILE, prepare the pasta according to the package directions. Add the cauliflower and squash in the last 5 minutes of the pasta cooking time. Drain the pasta and vegetables and immediately add to the sauce in the Dutch oven. Add the cheese and toss gently to combine.

TOTAL TIME: 40 minutes **MAKES 6 SERVINGS**

PER SERVING: 239 calories, 8 g protein, 44 g carbohydrates, 2 g total fat, 1 g saturated fat, 4 g fiber, 212 mg sodium

Fettuccine Alfredo with Peas

Beyond their health benefits to humans, green peas also stand out as an environmentally friendly food. Agricultural research has shown that pea crops can improve soil health by converting nitrogen in the air into other forms that enrich the soil and are more readily available to other plants.

1 tablespoon all-purpose flour

¼ teaspoon salt

⅛ teaspoon ground black pepper

1½ cups 1% milk, divided

¾ cup grated Parmesan cheese

1 teaspoon trans-free vegetable oil spread

6 ounces fettuccine

½ cup frozen green peas, thawed

WHISK together the flour, salt, pepper, and ½ cup of the milk in a medium saucepan over medium heat. Whisk in the remaining 1 cup milk. Bring to a slow simmer.

STIR in the cheese and spread. Cook, stirring regularly, for 3 to 4 minutes, or until the sauce is slightly thickened. Remove from the heat and cover to keep warm.

PREPARE the pasta according to the package directions. Place the peas in a colander. Drain the pasta over the peas. Immediately return the pasta and peas to the pot. Add the cheese sauce and toss gently to coat.

TOTAL TIME: 40 minutes **MAKES 4 SERVINGS**

PER SERVING: 282 calories, 16 g protein, 41 g carbohydrates, 6 g total fat, 3 g saturated fat, 2 g fiber, 444 mg sodium

Fettuccine with Pesto and Green Beans

Few dishes taste more like summer than this one. But by relying on frozen green beans, you can enjoy it practically any time of year.

8 ounces fettuccine

1½ cups frozen green beans

⅓ cup prepared pesto

¼ cup grated Parmesan cheese

¼ teaspoon salt

¼ teaspoon ground black pepper

PREPARE the pasta according to the package directions. Add the beans to the pot during the last 5 minutes of cooking time.

LADLE ½ cup of the cooking liquid into a small bowl and set aside. Drain the pasta and beans. Immediately return the pasta and beans to the pot and add the pesto, cheese, salt, pepper, and reserved cooking liquid. Stir to blend.

TOTAL TIME: 15 minutes **MAKES 4 SERVINGS**

PER SERVING: 348 calories, 14 g protein, 47 g carbohydrates, 12 g total fat, 4 g saturated fat, 4 g fiber, 383 mg sodium

Spicy Broccoli Noodles

If you prefer less spice, omit the red-pepper flakes in this dish. The results will still be fabulous.

2 teaspoons canola oil

1 package (14 ounces) tofu, drained and cut into ¾" cubes

¼ teaspoon salt

½ yellow bell pepper, seeded and chopped

1 tablespoon finely chopped fresh ginger

3 cloves garlic, minced

6 ounces linguine

3 cups broccoli florets

½ cup low-sodium vegetable broth

2 tablespoons less-sodium soy sauce

1 tablespoon hoisin sauce

½ teaspoon red-pepper flakes

HEAT the oil in a large nonstick skillet over medium-high heat. Add the tofu and cook for 6 to 8 minutes, turning once, or until golden brown. Sprinkle with the salt and add the bell pepper, ginger, and garlic. Cook, stirring, for 1 minute, or until fragrant. Remove the skillet from the heat and set aside.

MEANWHILE, prepare the pasta according to the package directions. Add the broccoli to the pot during the last 3 minutes of cooking time.

WHISK together the broth, soy sauce, hoisin sauce, and red-pepper flakes in a small bowl.

DRAIN the pasta and broccoli. Immediately return the pasta and broccoli to the pot and add the tofu mixture. Pour the broth mixture over the pasta mixture and toss to coat.

TOTAL TIME: 20 minutes **MAKES 4 SERVINGS**

PER SERVING: 298 calories, 17 g protein, 42 g carbohydrates, 8 g total fat, 1 g saturated fat, 4 g fiber, 515 mg sodium

Creamy Peanut Noodles

Cut the recipe in half if cooking for two or three people. This dish is best served at room temperature, and unlike most Asian noodle dishes, it doesn't reheat well.

12 ounces whole wheat spaghetti

½ cup creamy natural peanut butter

½ cup fat-free evaporated milk

3 tablespoons reduced-sodium soy sauce

1 teaspoon toasted sesame oil

1 small cucumber, peeled and thinly sliced

2 carrots, shredded

18 sugar snap peas

COOK the pasta according to the package directions.

MEANWHILE, combine the peanut butter, milk, soy sauce, and oil in a large bowl or blender. Using an immersion or regular blender, blend until smooth. Transfer to a large bowl, if necessary.

DRAIN the pasta. Rinse under cool running water to stop the cooking process. Add to the peanut butter mixture. Toss until evenly coated.

DIVIDE the pasta among 6 bowls. Top with the cucumber, carrots, and peas.

TOTAL TIME: 25 minutes **MAKES 6 SERVINGS**

PER SERVING: 378 calories, 16 g protein, 54 g carbohydrates, 12 g total fat, 2 g saturated fat, 10 g fiber, 428 mg sodium

WHY YOU SHOULD CHOOSE

Peanut butter

This American classic supplies protein and good fats, plus B vitamins, vitamin E, and a slew of minerals. It's perfect as a snack, in a main dish, or as a condiment. Peanut butter in moderate amounts is filling, helps stave off hunger, and feels like an indulgence.

Vegetable Fried Rice with Peas and Carrots

If you have time, go ahead and prepare the rice for this recipe a day ahead and refrigerate until you're ready to assemble the finished dish. Cold, cooked rice fries more evenly.

1⅓ cups short-grain brown rice

1 package (14 ounces) extra-firm tofu

1 tablespoon canola oil

½ teaspoon salt, divided

3 cloves garlic, chopped

2 jalapeño chile peppers, seeded and chopped (wear plastic gloves when handling)

1 piece (1") fresh ginger, peeled and chopped

2 carrots, chopped

2 cups frozen green peas, thawed and rinsed

1 red bell pepper, seeded and thinly sliced

4 scallions, thinly sliced

COOK the rice according to the package directions. Place the tofu between layers of paper towels and let stand for 30 minutes. Chop the tofu when it has given off most of its liquid.

HEAT the oil in a large nonstick skillet over medium-high heat. Add the tofu and cook for 6 to 8 minutes, turning once, or until golden brown. Sprinkle with ¼ teaspoon of the salt. With a slotted spoon, remove to a plate.

ADD the garlic, chile peppers, and ginger to the skillet and cook, stirring constantly, for 1 to 2 minutes, or until fragrant. Add the carrots, peas, and bell pepper and cook for 8 to 9 minutes, or until the vegetables start to soften. Stir in the tofu and cooked rice. Season with the remaining ¼ teaspoon salt and garnish with the scallions.

TOTAL TIME: 50 minutes **MAKES 4 SERVINGS**

PER SERVING: 454 calories, 20 g protein, 60 g carbohydrates, 11 g total fat, 1.5 g saturated fat, 10 g fiber, 403 mg sodium

Better-Than-Takeout Pad Thai

Craving some Thai food takeout tonight? Put down that phone and check your cupboard first. Odds are you have most of the ingredients you'll need to throw this dish together.

8 ounces rice-flour noodles

2 tablespoons reduced-sodium fish sauce

3 tablespoons firmly packed brown sugar

2 tablespoons less-sodium soy sauce

2 tablespoons fresh lime juice

1 tablespoon rice wine vinegar

½ teaspoon ground red pepper

3 teaspoons toasted sesame oil, divided

4 ounces tofu, drained and cubed

3 cloves garlic, minced

1 egg + 2 egg whites, lightly beaten

4 cups bean sprouts

4 scallions, both white and green parts, coarsely chopped

2 tablespoons roughly chopped roasted, unsalted peanuts

1 cup chopped fresh cilantro

PLACE the noodles in a microwaveable shallow dish and add just enough water to barely cover. Microwave on high power for 3 to 4 minutes, or until the noodles are soft. Set aside.

WHISK together the fish sauce, sugar, soy sauce, lime juice, vinegar, pepper, and 1 teaspoon of the oil in a small bowl. Set aside.

HEAT the remaining 2 teaspoons oil in a wok or large nonstick skillet over medium heat. When the oil is hot but not smoking, add the tofu and cook for 3 minutes, turning once, or until lightly browned. Add the garlic and cook for 1 to 2 minutes.

ADD the egg and egg whites. When just set, stir and gently push to the side of the skillet.

ADD the sprouts and stir gently just until barely combined with the tofu and eggs. Stir in the drained noodles, scallions, and fish sauce mixture and simmer for 5 to 10 minutes, or just until the liquid thickens slightly.

SERVE garnished with the peanuts and cilantro.

TOTAL TIME: 1 hour **MAKES 4 SERVINGS**

PER SERVING: 381 calories, 11 g protein, 68 g carbohydrates, 8 g total fat, 1 g saturated fat, 3 g fiber, 910 mg sodium

Coconut Curried Tofu
with Macadamia Nuts

Don't shy away from this dish because you think macadamia nuts and coconut milk can't help you lose weight. Good fats are essential in an ideal diet because they make food tasty and promote satiety.

1 cup brown basmati rice

1 package (14 ounces) tofu, drained and cut into ¾" cubes

1 tablespoon canola oil

½ teaspoon salt, divided

1 large onion, halved and thinly sliced

1–2 tablespoons red curry paste

½ teaspoon curry powder

4 cups broccoli florets

1 cup frozen green peas

1 cup light coconut milk

¾ cup reduced-sodium vegetable broth

1 large tomato, cut into ¾" pieces

2 tablespoons lime juice

¾ cup chopped macadamia nuts

COOK the rice according to the package directions.

HEAT the oil in a large nonstick skillet over medium-high heat. Add the tofu and cook for 6 to 8 minutes, turning once, or until golden brown. Sprinkle with ¼ teaspoon of the salt. With a slotted spoon, remove to a plate.

ADD the onion to the skillet and cook, stirring frequently, for 3 to 4 minutes, or until browned. Stir in 1 tablespoon curry paste, the curry powder, and remaining ¼ teaspoon salt. Taste and add more curry paste, if desired. Add the broccoli, peas, coconut milk, and broth. Bring to a boil.

REDUCE the heat to low. Cover and simmer for 3 to 4 minutes, or until the broccoli is tender-crisp. Stir in the tomato, lime juice, and tofu. Simmer, stirring occasionally, for 2 to 3 minutes, or until the tofu is heated through. Serve over the rice. Sprinkle with the macadamia nuts.

TOTAL TIME: 1 hour **MAKES 6 SERVINGS**

PER SERVING: 409 calories, 17 g protein, 37 g carbohydrates, 25 g total fat, 5.5 g saturated fat, 8 g fiber, 266 mg sodium

Roasted Hoisin Tofu

Serve with brown rice as a meatless main course alongside a lightly dressed salad of napa cabbage or cucumbers. Or let the tofu cool to room temperature, refrigerate, and then cut into cubes to use in a salad, soup, stew, or stir-fry.

2 packages (15 ounces each) extra-firm tofu

¼ cup hoisin sauce

2 tablespoons rice wine vinegar

1 tablespoon dark sesame oil

1 teaspoon Asian chili garlic sauce

PLACE the tofu between layers of paper towels and let stand for 30 minutes.

PREHEAT the oven to 375°F.

STIR together the hoisin sauce, vinegar, oil, and chili garlic sauce in a small bowl. Pat the tofu dry and brush with the hoisin mixture to coat. Place on a rimmed baking sheet. Roast for 45 to 50 minutes, flipping occasionally, or until browned and hot.

TOTAL TIME: 1 hour 20 minutes **MAKES 4 SERVINGS**

PER SERVING: 274 calories, 22 g protein, 13 g carbohydrates, 15 g total fat, 2 g saturated fat, 3 g fiber, 268 mg sodium

Tempeh Stir-Fry

Tempeh is made from cooked and slightly fermented soybeans and comes in patty form, similar to a very firm veggie burger. If you're not a tofu fan, don't assume you won't like tempeh. Its flavor and texture are distinctly different from the more bland nature of tofu.

- 2 tablespoons reduced-sodium soy sauce
- 1 tablespoon hoisin sauce
- 1 clove garlic, minced
- 3 teaspoons canola oil, divided
- 1 package (8 ounces) tempeh, cut into ¾" cubes
- 2 cups cauliflower florets
- ½ sweet onion, thinly sliced
- 2 tablespoons water
- 1 carrot, thinly sliced
- 1 cup snow peas
- 2 tablespoons chopped dry-roasted peanuts
- 2 cups cooked brown rice (optional)

STIR together the soy sauce, hoisin sauce, and garlic in a small bowl. Set aside.

HEAT 2 teaspoons of the oil in a large nonstick skillet over medium-high heat. Add the tempeh and cook for 6 to 8 minutes, turning once, or until golden brown. With a slotted spoon, remove to a plate.

HEAT the remaining 1 teaspoon oil in the same skillet. Add the cauliflower, onion, and water. Cook, covered, for 5 minutes, or until the cauliflower is tender. Add the carrot and peas. Cook, covered, for 3 minutes, or until the vegetables are tender.

ADD the tempeh and soy sauce mixture to the skillet and toss to coat. Top with the peanuts and serve over the brown rice, if desired.

TOTAL TIME: 30 minutes **MAKES 4 SERVINGS**

PER SERVING: 223 calories, 14 g protein, 17 g carbohydrates, 13 g total fat, 3 g saturated fat, 3 g fiber, 391 mg sodium

Mushroom, Onion, and Avocado Quesadillas

No one will miss the meat when you have hearty mushrooms and cheese standing in its place. If you are cooking for one, simply divide the mushroom mixture and save the leftovers for later in the week. To store an avocado, rub the cut sides with a few drops of olive oil and place in a resealable plastic bag (press tightly to remove as much air as possible). Refrigerate for up to 3 days.

1 tablespoon olive oil

1 large onion, chopped

1 package (8 ounces) sliced mushrooms

¼ teaspoon salt

4 cloves garlic, minced

1 avocado, peeled, pitted, and mashed

2 tablespoons chopped fresh cilantro

4 flour tortillas (8" diameter)

1 cup (4 ounces) shredded reduced-fat sharp Cheddar cheese

HEAT the oil in a large nonstick skillet over medium-high heat. Add the onion, mushrooms, and salt. Cook, stirring occasionally, for 9 to 10 minutes, or until browned. Stir in the garlic and cook for 2 minutes. Remove from the heat.

COMBINE the avocado and cilantro in a bowl. Arrange the tortillas in a single layer on a work surface. Spread the bottom half of each tortilla with one-fourth of the avocado mixture. Top each with 2 tablespoons of the cheese and one-fourth of the onion mixture. Sprinkle each with 2 tablespoons of the remaining cheese. Fold the top half of each tortilla over the filling.

WIPE out the skillet and place over medium heat. Add 2 quesadillas and cook for 3 to 4 minutes per side, or until the filling is hot and the outside is lightly browned. Repeat with the remaining quesadillas. Transfer to a cutting board and cut each in half before serving.

TOTAL TIME: 40 minutes **MAKES 4**

PER QUESADILLA: 367 calories, 14 g protein, 35 g carbohydrates, 21 g total fat, 5 g saturated fat, 6 g fiber, 680 mg sodium

Cheese Enchiladas

Carrots are the surprise ingredient in the spicy sauce for these enchiladas. They add natural sweetness and beta-carotene.

2 teaspoons olive oil

3 large carrots, chopped

⅓ cup water

1 can (14.5 ounces) crushed tomatoes

1 large onion, quartered

2 chipotle peppers in adobo sauce

½ teaspoon salt

2 cups canned no-salt-added cannellini beans, rinsed and drained

12 corn tortillas (6" diameter)

2 cups (8 ounces) shredded reduced-fat Mexican-blend cheese, divided

1 can (4.5 ounces) chopped mild green chiles, drained

PREHEAT the oven to 350°F.

HEAT the oil in a large skillet over medium heat. Add the carrots and water and cook, stirring frequently, for 5 minutes, or until tender.

COMBINE the carrots and any liquid in the skillet with the tomatoes, onion, peppers, and salt in a food processor or blender. Process until smooth. Return the puree to the skillet and cook over medium heat, stirring occasionally, for 10 minutes, or until the sauce thickens.

MASH the beans with either a potato masher or the back of a spoon. Spoon ½ cup of the sauce into the bottom of an 11" × 7" baking dish.

DIP both sides of each tortilla briefly in the sauce. Spread the beans down the middle of each tortilla. Sprinkle half of the cheese and all of the green chiles over the beans. Roll up the tortillas and arrange, seam sides down, in the baking dish. Spoon the remaining sauce over the tortillas. Sprinkle the remaining cheese on top.

COVER and bake for 25 minutes, or until piping hot and bubbling.

TOTAL TIME: 1 hour MAKES 12

PER SERVING (2 ENCHILADAS): 392 calories, 18 g protein, 47 g carbohydrates, 15 g total fat, 7.5 g saturated fat, 9 g fiber, 656 mg sodium

Meatless Tacos

Who doesn't love taco night? This colorful spread is so tasty and satisfying it's sure to become a family favorite.

2½ cups water

8 ounces brown lentils, rinsed

1 tablespoon vegetable oil

½ onion, chopped

3 cloves garlic, minced

2 tablespoons chili powder

1¼ cups salsa, divided

12 flour tortillas (6" diameter)

1 avocado, peeled, pitted, and mashed

1 cup shredded romaine lettuce

4 radishes, halved and thinly sliced

⅓ cup fat-free sour cream

2 scallions, thinly sliced

COMBINE the water and lentils in a large nonstick skillet. Cover and bring to a boil. Reduce the heat and cook for 12 minutes, or until the water is almost absorbed.

MEANWHILE, heat the oil in a Dutch oven over medium-high heat. Cook the onion for 5 minutes, or until tender. Add the garlic and chili powder and cook for 30 seconds, or until fragrant. Stir ½ cup of the salsa and the cooked lentils into the onion mixture. Reduce the heat to low and simmer for 5 minutes, or until most of the liquid evaporates.

SERVE the lentil mixture alongside the remaining ¾ cup salsa, tortillas, avocado, lettuce, radishes, sour cream, and scallions.

TOTAL TIME: 30 minutes   **MAKES 12**

PER SERVING (2 TACOS): 410 calories, 17 g protein, 62 g carbohydrates, 11 g total fat, 2 g saturated fat, 15 g fiber, 727 mg sodium

Seafood

CHAPTER
11

Fish and Chips

This recipe features two twists on the age-old classic: Panko bread crumbs give an excellent crunch to the oven-fried halibut in lieu of a deep-fried batter, while sweet potato chips (instead of the russet potato variety) pack in fiber, beta-carotene, and a ton of flavor.

2 sweet potatoes, peeled and cut lengthwise into wedges

1½ teaspoons olive oil

½ teaspoon smoked paprika

⅛ teaspoon salt

¼ teaspoon ground black pepper, divided

2 egg whites

1 teaspoon Dijon mustard

⅛ teaspoon ground red pepper

1 cup panko bread crumbs

½ teaspoon dried thyme

4 skinless halibut fillets (6 ounces each)

Lemon wedges or malt vinegar (optional)

PREHEAT the oven to 425°F. Line 2 large baking sheets with parchment paper.

COMBINE the potatoes, oil, paprika, salt, and ⅛ teaspoon of the black pepper in a large bowl, tossing well to coat. Arrange on one of the baking sheets in a single layer. Bake for 30 minutes, turning once, or until browned and cooked through. Remove from the oven and keep warm.

MEANWHILE, whisk the egg whites, mustard, red pepper, and remaining ⅛ teaspoon black pepper in a medium bowl. Combine the bread crumbs and thyme in a shallow dish. Working with one fillet at a time, dip the halibut in the egg white mixture, shake off the excess, and roll in the bread crumb mixture to coat. Place on the second baking sheet.

BAKE the halibut for 12 minutes, turning once, or until the crumbs are golden brown and the fish flakes easily. Divide the fish and potatoes among 4 plates. Serve with the lemon wedges or malt vinegar, if desired.

TOTAL TIME: 45 minutes **MAKES 4 SERVINGS**

PER SERVING: 302 calories, 39 g protein, 20 g carbohydrates, 6 g total fat, 1 g saturated fat, 3 g fiber, 319 mg sodium

Lemon-Oregano Grilled Tilapia with Parsley Rice

Tilapia and other white-fleshed fish are relatively low in calories, making them an ideal source of protein to aid weight loss.

4 tilapia fillets
  (6 ounces each)

2 tablespoons lemon juice

1 tablespoon olive oil

2 teaspoons grated
  lemon peel

1 teaspoon dried oregano

¼ teaspoon salt

⅛ teaspoon ground
  black pepper

1½ cups instant brown rice

¼ cup chopped fresh parsley

COMBINE the tilapia, lemon juice, oil, lemon peel, oregano, salt, and pepper in a large bowl. Turn the tilapia to coat and let stand for 10 minutes.

HEAT a grill pan coated with cooking spray over medium-high heat. Remove the tilapia from the marinade. Place the tilapia on the grill pan and cook for 4 minutes per side, or until the fish flakes easily. (Cook in batches, if necessary.) Transfer to a serving plate.

MEANWHILE, prepare the rice according to the package directions. Transfer the rice to a bowl, add the parsley, and fluff with a fork to combine. Divide the rice and fillets among 4 plates.

TOTAL TIME: 30 minutes **MAKES 4 SERVINGS**

PER SERVING: 282 calories, 36 g protein, 17 g carbohydrates, 8 g total fat, 2 g saturated fat, 1 g fiber, 238 mg sodium

Roasted Catfish
with Cumin Sweet Potatoes

The fact that it is delicious is not the only reason to enjoy catfish. Because they are raised in closed, inland ponds and fed a mostly vegetarian diet, US farmed catfish are considered to be one of the most sustainable fish species available.

2 large sweet potatoes, peeled and sliced ¼" thick

½ teaspoon ground cumin

1 tablespoon canola oil

4 catfish fillets (6 ounces each)

½ cup diagonally sliced scallions

1 teaspoon chili powder

1 bag (10 ounces) frozen corn kernels, thawed

1 green bell pepper, seeded and chopped

2 tablespoons lime juice

1 tablespoon chopped fresh cilantro

1 teaspoon finely chopped jalapeño chile pepper (wear plastic gloves when handling)

PREHEAT the oven to 400°F. Place the potatoes in a 13" × 9" baking dish. Sprinkle with the cumin, drizzle with the oil, and toss to coat. Spread in an even layer and roast for 45 minutes, or until the potatoes are browned.

REMOVE from the oven. Increase the oven temperature to 450°F. Use a wide spatula to gently turn the potato slices. Arrange the fish on top of the potatoes. Sprinkle with the scallions and chili powder.

RETURN the baking dish to the oven and roast until the fish flakes easily, 8 to 10 minutes per inch of thickness.

MEANWHILE, combine the corn, bell pepper, lime juice, cilantro, and chile pepper in a medium bowl.

LIFT a portion of the potatoes with a fillet on top onto each of 4 plates using a wide spatula. Spoon the corn salad on top.

TOTAL TIME: 1 hour 10 minutes **MAKES 4 SERVINGS**

PER SERVING: 404 calories, 31 g protein, 34 g carbohydrates, 17 g total fat, 3 g saturated fat, 5 g fiber, 143 mg sodium

Halibut with Asparagus, Onion, and Lemon

While this dish is typically prepared using parchment paper, feel free to substitute aluminum foil, which works just as well and is easier to seal.

1 red onion, thinly sliced

4 teaspoons olive oil

4 skinless halibut fillets (6 ounces each)

¾ pound asparagus, trimmed

1 plum tomato, seeded and chopped

2 tablespoons lemon juice

¼ teaspoon salt

⅛ teaspoon ground black pepper

¼ cup fresh basil leaves, thinly sliced

PREHEAT the oven to 450°F. Cut four 18" × 12" sheets of parchment paper or foil.

COAT 1 sheet of the paper or foil with cooking spray. Fold the sheet in half from short end to short end, then open. Place one-fourth of the onion in the center of the right half of the sheet. Drizzle with ¼ teaspoon oil. Top the onion with a fillet. Place one-fourth of the asparagus next to the halibut and sprinkle one-fourth of the tomato over both. Drizzle with ¾ teaspoon oil and ½ tablespoon lemon juice. Repeat with the remaining sheets of parchment paper or foil, onion, oil, halibut, asparagus, tomato, and lemon juice.

SPRINKLE all the packets with the salt and pepper. Fold the paper or foil over the halibut mixture, as if closing a book, then tightly crimp the edges to seal the packets.

ARRANGE the packets on a large baking sheet and bake for 12 minutes, or until the packets have expanded and are puffy. Remove from the oven and place 1 packet on each of 4 serving plates. Cut a cross in the top of each packet with the tip of a knife and carefully fold back the paper or foil, being mindful of the steam, and sprinkle with the basil.

TOTAL TIME: 35 minutes **MAKES 4 SERVINGS**

PER SERVING: 255 calories, 37 g protein, 6 g carbohydrates, 9 g total fat, 1 g saturated fat, 2 g fiber, 240 mg sodium

Roast Cod with Pomegranate-Walnut Sauce

Nutritional benefits aside, quinoa is a great alternative to rice because it cooks in half the time and expands to four times its original volume.

1 cup black or regular quinoa

1 tablespoon olive oil

1 shallot, finely chopped

⅓ cup ground walnuts

3 cloves garlic, minced

⅓ cup dry red wine

¼ cup reduced-sodium chicken broth

1½ tablespoons pomegranate molasses or frozen cranberry juice concentrate

1 tablespoon honey

4 cod fillets (6 ounces each)

¼ teaspoon salt

⅛ teaspoon ground black pepper

¼ cup chopped fresh parsley

¼ cup broken walnut halves

PREPARE the quinoa according to the package directions.

MEANWHILE, heat the oil in a nonstick skillet over medium heat. Add the shallot and cook, stirring occasionally, for 2 minutes, or until softened. Add the ground walnuts and garlic and cook, stirring occasionally, for 4 minutes, or until the ground walnuts are golden brown. Remove from the heat and add the wine, broth, molasses or cranberry juice concentrate, and honey. Simmer, stirring occasionally, for 4 minutes, or until the mixture has thickened. Cover and keep warm.

PREHEAT the broiler. Season the fillets with the salt and pepper, and arrange in a single layer on a baking sheet lined with nonstick foil. Broil for 6 minutes, or until the fish flakes easily.

TOSS the quinoa with the parsley and broken walnuts. Spoon onto 4 plates and top with the fish and sauce.

TOTAL TIME: 30 minutes **MAKES 4 SERVINGS**

PER SERVING: 481 calories, 39 g protein, 43 g carbohydrates, 16 g total fat, 1.5 g saturated fat, 5 g fiber, 137 mg sodium

Seared Tuna Tacos with Avocado Salsa

Cooking fish over high heat gives it a nice brown coating. Avoid overcrowding the skillet, which reduces the temperature of the pan and creates steam—both will prevent proper searing.

4 **whole wheat tortillas (8" diameter)**

2 **tomatoes, chopped**

2 **ripe avocados, peeled, pitted, and chopped**

1 **green bell pepper, seeded and chopped**

¼ **cup chopped fresh cilantro**

2 **tablespoons + 2 teaspoons lime juice**

½ **teaspoon salt**

2 **teaspoons ground cumin**

½ **teaspoon garlic powder**

2 **ahi tuna steaks (8 ounces each)**

PREHEAT the oven to 250°F.

WRAP the tortillas in a piece of foil and place in the oven to warm for 10 minutes.

COMBINE the tomatoes, avocados, pepper, cilantro, 2 tablespoons of the lime juice, and salt in a small bowl. Set aside.

COMBINE the cumin, garlic powder, and remaining 2 teaspoons lime juice in a small bowl. Rub onto the tuna.

HEAT a large nonstick skillet coated with cooking spray over high heat. Add the tuna and cook for 3 to 6 minutes, turning once, or until the fish is cooked to desired doneness. Slice.

PLACE each tortilla on a plate. Divide the tuna and avocado salsa among the tortillas. Fold and serve immediately.

TOTAL TIME: 20 minutes **MAKES 4**

PER TACO: 387 calories, 33 g protein, 33 g carbohydrates, 18 g total fat, 3 g saturated fat, 6 g fiber, 513 mg sodium

WHY YOU SHOULD CHOOSE

Avocados

Avocado is worth every calorie for its flavor, creamy texture, and vitamin-packed flesh. Its versatility as a spread or a dip (plain or mixed with tomato and seasonings for guacamole) and a topper for salads and sandwiches is hard to match.

Glazed Salmon
with Broiled Pineapple Slaw

Luscious, tart-sweet pineapple is full of nutrients as well as flavor. In addition to supplying vitamin C, a cup contains your daily quota of manganese, a trace mineral that promotes bone health.

4 salmon fillets
(5 ounces each)

½ cup pineapple chunks

1 tablespoon lime juice

1 tablespoon honey

1½ cups thinly sliced cabbage

1 carrot, grated

1 tablespoon roasted or
raw sunflower seeds

1 tablespoon chopped
fresh cilantro

PREHEAT the broiler. Line the rack of a broiler pan with foil and coat with cooking spray.

ARRANGE the salmon and pineapple on the foil.

COMBINE the lime juice and honey in a small bowl. Drizzle 2 teaspoons over the salmon and pineapple. Set aside the remaining lime juice mixture.

BROIL the salmon and pineapple for 6 to 7 minutes, or just until the fish is opaque and the pineapple is lightly browned.

MEANWHILE, combine the cabbage, carrot, sunflower seeds, and cilantro in a large bowl.

ADD the broiled pineapple to the cabbage mixture and toss with the reserved lime juice mixture. Serve the fish with the slaw on the side.

TOTAL TIME: 20 minutes **MAKES 4 SERVINGS**

PER SERVING: 350 calories, 30 g protein, 11 g carbohydrates, 20 g total fat, 4.5 g saturated fat, 2 g fiber, 111 mg sodium

Seared Scallops
with White Beans and Bacon

Scallops without any additives are called dry packed, while scallops treated with sodium tripolyphosphate are called wet packed. Dry-packed scallops will brown much better in a dish like this.

- **2 slices center-cut bacon,** chopped into small pieces
- **½ red onion, finely chopped**
- **1 clove garlic, minced**
- **1½ cans (14 ounces each) white beans, rinsed and drained**
- **4 cups fresh baby spinach**
- **1 tablespoon butter**
- **1 pound large sea scallops,** preferably dry packed
- **¼ teaspoon salt, divided**
- **¼ teaspoon ground black pepper, divided**
- **2 tablespoons fresh lemon juice**

HEAT a medium saucepan over low heat and cook the bacon until it begins to crisp.

POUR off most of the bacon fat and add the onion and garlic to the saucepan. Cook for 2 to 3 minutes, or until the onion is soft and translucent. Add the beans and spinach and cook until the beans are heated through and the spinach wilts. Keep warm.

MELT the butter in a large nonstick skillet over medium-high heat. Blot the scallops dry with a paper towel and season on both sides with ⅛ teaspoon of the salt and ⅛ teaspoon of the pepper. Sear the scallops for 2 to 3 minutes per side, or until well browned and opaque in the center.

ADD the lemon juice, remaining ⅛ teaspoon salt, and remaining ⅛ teaspoon pepper to the bean mixture just before serving. Divide the bean mixture among 4 warm bowls or plates and top with the scallops.

TOTAL TIME: 20 minutes **MAKES 4 SERVINGS**

PER SERVING: 284 calories, 28 g protein, 28 g carbohydrates, 6 g total fat, 2.5 g saturated fat, 7 g fiber, 400 mg sodium

Jamaican-Style Scallops with Black Bean Salsa

Caribbean flavors have become so popular that you can probably find a seasoning mix in the spice aisle of your grocery store instead of in the international foods section.

- 1 **can (14.5 ounces) no-salt-added black beans, rinsed and drained**
- 1 **tomato, chopped**
- 1 **red bell pepper, seeded and chopped**
- 1 **mango, peeled and cubed**
- ½ **red onion, finely chopped**
- 1 **small jalapeño chile pepper, seeded and finely chopped (wear plastic gloves when handling)**
- 2 **tablespoons lime juice**
- 2 **tablespoons canola oil, divided**
- 1 **tablespoon chopped fresh cilantro**
- ¼ **teaspoon ground cumin**
- ⅛ **teaspoon salt**
   Ground black pepper
- 1 **pound large sea scallops, preferably dry packed**
- 1 **teaspoon Caribbean jerk seasoning**
- ½ **cup macadamia nuts, chopped**
- 4 **lime wedges**

COMBINE the beans, tomato, bell pepper, mango, onion, chile pepper, lime juice, 1 tablespoon of the oil, cilantro, cumin, and salt in a medium bowl, mixing well. Add the black pepper to taste. Let stand to allow the flavors to blend.

HEAT the remaining 1 tablespoon oil in a large nonstick skillet over medium-high heat. Blot the scallops dry with a paper towel and dust with the jerk seasoning. Sear the scallops for 2 to 3 minutes per side, or until well browned and opaque in the center. Remove to a plate.

SPOON the salsa onto 4 dinner plates. Top with the scallops and scatter 2 tablespoons nuts over each serving. Garnish with a lime wedge.

TOTAL TIME: 45 minutes **MAKES 4 SERVINGS**

PER SERVING: 383 calories, 24 g protein, 29 g carbohydrates, 21 g total fat, 3 g saturated fat, 7 g fiber, 562 mg sodium

Garlic Shrimp and Kale Stir-Fry

Simple to throw together, this tasty stir-fry is sure to become part of your weeknight repertoire.

1 **cup quick-cooking brown rice**

3 **teaspoons toasted sesame oil, divided**

1 **pound peeled and deveined medium shrimp**

1 **onion, chopped**

4 **cloves garlic, sliced**

3 **scallions, sliced**

2 **carrots, thinly sliced**

6 **cups chopped kale**

½ **cup reduced-sodium chicken broth**

1 **tablespoon hoisin sauce**

PREPARE the rice according to the package directions, omitting any fat.

MEANWHILE, heat 1 teaspoon of the oil in a large nonstick skillet over medium-high heat. Cook the shrimp for 3 minutes, turning once, or until just opaque. Transfer to a plate.

HEAT the remaining 2 teaspoons oil in the same skillet over medium heat. Cook the onion, garlic, scallions, and carrots for 2 minutes, or until the vegetables just start to soften. Add the kale and cook for 2 minutes. Add the broth and cook, stirring occasionally, for 3 minutes, or until the kale wilts. Stir in the cooked shrimp and hoisin sauce. Cook for 1 minute, stirring occasionally, or until heated through. Serve over the rice.

TOTAL TIME: 25 minutes **MAKES 4 SERVINGS**

PER SERVING: 318 calories, 30 g protein, 37 g carbohydrates, 7 g total fat, 1 g saturated fat, 5 g fiber, 311 mg sodium

Find the Fiber

The top foods for fiber are canned and dried beans, along with fruits and vegetables, whole grains, and cereals and breads that list a whole grain as the first ingredient. A standard portion of beans is about ½ cup cooked, the size of a tennis ball. Our portions of cooked pasta, rice, and other grains range from ⅓ cup to ⅔ cup, depending on the number of calories in the other foods in the meal. When you are buying dry pasta, figure on at least eight servings in a pound.

Shrimp Scampi Linguine

Cherry tomatoes and spinach lend more nutritional value, as well as flavor, to this classic dish. If you don't enjoy the soft texture of cooked spinach, kale or arugula would provide a sturdier substitute.

- **9 ounces whole wheat linguine**
- **1 tablespoon extra-virgin olive oil**
- **1 pound peeled and deveined medium shrimp**
- **4 cloves garlic, minced**
- **½ teaspoon red-pepper flakes**
- **1 pint cherry tomatoes, halved**
- **½ cup dry white wine**
- **2 tablespoons fresh lemon juice**
- **½ teaspoon salt**
- **3 cups packed fresh baby spinach**
- **¼ cup finely chopped fresh parsley**
- **¼ cup grated Parmesan cheese**

PREPARE the pasta according to the package directions.

MEANWHILE, heat the oil in a large skillet over medium heat. Add the shrimp, garlic, and red-pepper flakes and cook for 2 minutes, or until the shrimp start to turn opaque.

ADD the tomatoes, wine, lemon juice, and salt. Cook for 1 minute, or until the tomatoes start to soften. Add the spinach and parsley and cook for 1 minute, or until the spinach wilts.

DRAIN the pasta and add to the skillet. Toss to coat and serve sprinkled with the cheese.

TOTAL TIME: 25 minutes **MAKES 4 SERVINGS**

PER SERVING: 449 calories, 36 g protein, 57 g carbohydrates, 8 g total fat, 2 g saturated fat, 7 g fiber, 576 mg sodium

Walnut Shrimp Stir-Fry

There are hundreds of reasons to love stir-fries, but the fact that they are so quick to prepare is among the best.

2 tablespoons medium-dry sherry (optional)

1 tablespoon reduced-sodium soy sauce

1 pound peeled and deveined shrimp

½ cup walnuts, coarsely chopped

2 tablespoons canola oil

2 tablespoons chopped fresh ginger

½ cup reduced-sodium, fat-free chicken broth

3 scallions, whites thinly sliced diagonally, greens diagonally sliced into 1" pieces

1 tablespoon honey

1 teaspoon rice wine vinegar

1½ teaspoons cornstarch, dissolved in 1 tablespoon water

MIX the sherry, if using, and soy sauce in a medium bowl. Add the shrimp and toss to coat. Let stand for 10 minutes. Drain the shrimp, reserving the marinade.

MEANWHILE, toast the walnuts in a large heavy skillet over medium-high heat, tossing frequently, for 5 minutes, or until fragrant. Place on a plate. Wipe out the skillet.

ADD the oil and ginger to the same skillet and cook, stirring frequently, for 1 minute, or until the ginger is fragrant. Add the shrimp and cook, stirring occasionally, for 3 to 4 minutes, or until opaque. Add the broth, scallions, and reserved marinade and bring to a boil. Boil for 1 minute.

ADD the honey and vinegar. Stir in the cornstarch mixture and cook, stirring constantly, for 1 minute, or until thickened and bubbly. Remove from the heat and stir in the walnuts.

TOTAL TIME: 40 minutes **MAKES 4 SERVINGS**

PER SERVING: 307 calories, 26 g protein, 10 g carbohydrates, 19 g total fat, 2 g saturated fat, 1 g fiber, 378 mg sodium

Spicy Shrimp and Squash Sauté

Want another reason to enjoy a dish like this? Shrimp is a surprising source of vitamin D, which research shows may offer big benefits in bone health and cancer protection.

2 tablespoons pine nuts

1 tablespoon olive oil

3 plum tomatoes, chopped

4 small yellow squash, chopped

⅛ teaspoon salt

⅛ teaspoon ground black pepper

1 pound peeled and deveined medium shrimp

2 cloves garlic, minced

Splash of white wine (optional)

⅛ teaspoon red-pepper flakes

2 tablespoons chopped fresh basil, divided

¼ cup grated Parmesan cheese

TOAST the pine nuts in a large nonstick skillet over medium-high heat, tossing frequently, until fragrant. Place on a plate and set aside.

HEAT the oil in the same skillet. Add the tomatoes and squash. Season with the salt and black pepper. Cook, stirring often, for 5 to 7 minutes, or until the squash begins to soften.

ADD the shrimp, garlic, wine (if using), and red-pepper flakes. Cook for 5 to 6 minutes, turning the shrimp halfway through, or until opaque and firm. Stir in the toasted pine nuts and 1 tablespoon of the basil. Scatter the cheese and remaining 1 tablespoon basil on top before serving.

TOTAL TIME: 40 minutes **MAKES 4 SERVINGS**

PER SERVING: 239 calories, 29 g protein, 8 g carbohydrates, 11 g total fat, 2 g saturated fat, 2 g fiber, 371 mg sodium

Poultry

CHAPTER
12

Tequila-Lime Chicken with Avocado–Black Bean Salsa

For a hotter salsa, chop some of the ribs and seeds of the jalapeño chile pepper and add to taste. However, it's a good idea to wear plastic gloves when handling. The oil from the pepper can linger on your skin and become extremely irritating.

CHICKEN AND MARINADE

- ⅓ cup orange juice
- 3 tablespoons tequila or orange juice
- 2 cloves garlic, minced
- 1 teaspoon grated lime peel
- 1 teaspoon ground cumin
- 4 boneless, skinless chicken breast halves (5 ounces each)

SALSA

- 2 tomatoes, chopped
- 1 avocado, peeled, pitted, and chopped
- ¾ cup canned no-salt-added black beans, rinsed and drained
- 2 tablespoons chopped fresh cilantro
- 2 teaspoons chopped jalapeño chile pepper
- 2 tablespoons lime juice
- ¼ teaspoon ground cumin
- ⅛ teaspoon salt

TO MAKE THE CHICKEN AND MARINADE

COMBINE the orange juice, tequila or additional orange juice, garlic, lime peel, and cumin in a large resealable plastic bag. Shake to thoroughly combine. Add the chicken, push out all the air, and seal. Marinate in the refrigerator for 30 minutes.

COAT a grill rack or grill pan with cooking spray. Preheat the grill or grill pan to medium heat. Remove the chicken from the marinade and discard the marinade. Grill the chicken for 8 minutes, turning once, or until a thermometer inserted in the thickest portion registers 165°F and the juices run clear.

TO MAKE THE SALSA

TOSS together the tomatoes, avocado, beans, cilantro, pepper, lime juice, cumin, and salt in a large bowl. Serve with the chicken.

TOTAL TIME: 40 minutes **MAKES 4 SERVINGS**

PER SERVING: 280 calories, 37 g protein, 14 g carbohydrates, 9 g total fat, 2 g saturated fat, 6 g fiber, 250 mg sodium

Chicken with Avocado-Orange Salsa

Poaching the chicken ensures that it will stay moist and juicy. Add a few extra breasts to the poaching liquid if you like and use them later for sandwiches or wraps.

4 boneless, skinless chicken breast halves (5 ounces each)

4 cups water

½ teaspoon + ⅛ teaspoon salt

1 cup mandarin orange segments packed in water or juice

1 cup chopped avocado

4 radishes, thinly sliced

¼ cup chopped fresh basil + additional for garnish

COMBINE the chicken, water, and ½ teaspoon of the salt in a large saucepan. Cover and bring to a gentle boil over high heat. Reduce the heat and simmer for 15 minutes, or until a thermometer inserted in the thickest portion registers 165°F.

PLACE the orange segments in a medium bowl. Add the avocado, radishes, ¼ cup basil, and remaining ⅛ teaspoon salt. Gently toss to combine.

DRAIN the chicken, discarding the liquid. Let cool for 5 minutes. Cut crosswise into ½"-thick slices. Divide the orange mixture among 4 plates and top evenly with the chicken, drizzling the chicken with juice from the orange mixture. Garnish with additional basil, if desired.

TOTAL TIME: 25 minutes **MAKES 4 SERVINGS**

PER SERVING: 279 calories, 37 g protein, 10 g carbohydrates, 10 g total fat, 2 g saturated fat, 3 g fiber, 581 mg sodium

Grilled Jerk Chicken

Allspice is a versatile spice that lives up to its name. It has hints of cinnamon, clove, and nutmeg, all rolled into one enticing flavor.

¼ cup white wine vinegar

4 cloves garlic, minced

1 large pickled jalapeño chile pepper, minced

2 tablespoons firmly packed light brown sugar

2 tablespoons vegetable oil

1 tablespoon finely chopped fresh ginger

1 tablespoon ground allspice

1¼ teaspoons ground black pepper

¾ teaspoon salt

4 boneless, skinless chicken breast halves (5 ounces each)

COMBINE the vinegar, garlic, chile pepper, sugar, oil, ginger, allspice, black pepper, and salt in a large bowl. Add the chicken and turn to coat on all sides.

COVER and marinate in the refrigerator for 1 hour. (Don't marinate longer than 1 hour or the chicken will start to get mushy.)

PREHEAT the grill. Remove the chicken from the marinade and discard the marinade. Grill the chicken for 10 to 15 minutes, turning once, or until a thermometer inserted in the thickest portion registers 165°F and the juices run clear.

TOTAL TIME: 1 hour 20 minutes **MAKES 4 SERVINGS**

PER SERVING: 226 calories, 33 g protein, 6 g carbohydrates, 7 g total fat, 1 g saturated fat, 1 g fiber, 579 mg sodium

Spot the Sugar

Foods that you might not think of as overly sweet, such as ketchup, barbecue sauce, salad dressing, and breakfast cereals, often have added sweeteners (which give you unnecessary, nutrition-free calories). To spot the sugar, look for one of these listed in the top three ingredients:

sugar	glucose
corn syrup	sucrose
evaporated cane juice	fructose
fruit juice	maltodextrin
fruit juice concentrate	dextrose
honey	

BBQ Chicken
with Watermelon Salad

When fresh corn is in season, grill two ears of corn and then cut the kernels off the cob to use in this refreshing salad.

BBQ SAUCE

- ½ cup canned no-salt-added tomato puree
- ⅓ cup ketchup
- 3 tablespoons cider vinegar
- 1 tablespoon molasses
- 2 teaspoons Worcestershire sauce
- ½ onion, grated
- 1 teaspoon chili powder
- ½ teaspoon smoked paprika
- ¼ teaspoon mustard powder
- ¼ teaspoon salt

CHICKEN AND SALAD

- 4 boneless, skinless chicken breast halves (5 ounces each)
- 2 cups cubed watermelon
- 1 cup frozen corn kernels, thawed
- ½ cup shelled edamame, cooked
- 1 tablespoon fresh lime juice
- 1 tablespoon honey

TO MAKE THE BBQ SAUCE

COMBINE the tomato puree, ketchup, vinegar, molasses, Worcestershire sauce, onion, chili powder, paprika, mustard powder, and salt in a deep, enameled or stainless steel saucepan. Bring to a simmer and cook, stirring occasionally, for 15 minutes, or until thickened and reduced to about ¾ cup. Place half of the sauce in a serving bowl and set aside.

TO MAKE THE CHICKEN AND SALAD

COAT a grill rack or grill pan with cooking spray. Preheat the grill or grill pan. Grill the chicken for 8 minutes, turning once, or until a thermometer inserted in the thickest portion registers 165°F and the juices run clear. Brush the chicken with the remaining half of the BBQ sauce during the last 4 minutes of grilling.

MEANWHILE, toss together the watermelon, corn, edamame, lime juice, and honey in a medium bowl. Serve the salad with the grilled chicken and the reserved BBQ sauce.

TOTAL TIME: 35 minutes **MAKES 4 SERVINGS**

PER SERVING: 314 calories, 35 g protein, 33 g carbohydrates, 5 g total fat, 1 g saturated fat, 3 g fiber, 581 mg sodium

Italian Chicken Roll-Ups

Succulent chicken breasts are pounded and stuffed with a savory spinach filling to create this company-worthy dish. Serve with whole wheat orzo or mashed potatoes.

2 cups fresh baby spinach

¼ cup grated Parmesan cheese

¼ cup finely chopped onion

2 teaspoons olive oil, divided

1 teaspoon minced garlic

¼ teaspoon red-pepper flakes

1 tablespoon water

2 tablespoons chopped dry-packed sun-dried tomatoes

4 boneless, skinless chicken breast halves (5 ounces each), pounded to ¼" thickness

½ cup chicken broth or dry white wine

PLACE the spinach in a large microwaveable bowl with 1 to 2 tablespoons water. Cover and microwave on high power for 2 minutes, or until wilted. Drain or squeeze dry. Return the spinach to the bowl. Add the cheese and set aside.

MEANWHILE, combine the onion, 1 teaspoon of the oil, garlic, red-pepper flakes, and water in a large nonstick skillet. Cook over medium heat for 2 minutes. Reduce the heat to low. Cover and cook, stirring once, for 3 minutes, or until softened. Combine the onion mixture with the spinach mixture.

SCATTER the tomatoes evenly over the smooth side of each piece of chicken and top with the spinach mixture. Spread to the edges of 3 sides, leaving about 1" at the narrow tip free of spinach mixture. Loosely roll up the chicken, ending with the narrow tip, and secure with wooden picks.

HEAT the remaining 1 teaspoon oil in the same skillet over medium heat. Add the chicken and cook, turning occasionally, for 10 minutes, or until golden brown on all sides. Add the broth or wine, cover, and cook over low heat for 7 minutes. Uncover and transfer the chicken to a serving platter.

BOIL the skillet juices for 5 minutes, or until reduced to a glaze. Diagonally slice the chicken into 1"-thick pieces. Drizzle with skillet juices and serve.

TOTAL TIME: 40 minutes **MAKES 4 SERVINGS**

PER SERVING: 222 calories, 33 g protein, 4 g carbohydrates, 8 g total fat, 2 g saturated fat, 1 g fiber, 367 mg sodium

Chicken Cutlets Pomodoro

In Italian, the word for tomato is *pomodoro*, which literally translates to "golden apple." According to food historians, the first tomatoes in Italy were a yellowish color, but these days, the description al *pomodoro* on a menu indicates that a dish is served with a tomato sauce.

½ cup all-purpose flour, divided

1 egg, beaten

¼ cup + 2 tablespoons dry bread crumbs

¼ cup grated Parmesan cheese

4 boneless, skinless chicken breast halves (5 ounces each), pounded to ¼" thickness

2 tablespoons olive oil, divided

2 tablespoons grated or finely chopped onion

2 tablespoons sugar, divided

2 cloves garlic, grated or minced

1 cup chicken broth

2 tablespoons tomato paste

¼ teaspoon salt

⅛ teaspoon ground black pepper

PREHEAT the oven to 400°F. Line a baking sheet with parchment paper.

PLACE ¼ cup plus 2 tablespoons of the flour in a shallow bowl and the egg in another shallow dish. Mix the bread crumbs and cheese in a third shallow bowl. Dredge the chicken in the flour and dip in the egg, then in the bread crumb mixture.

HEAT 1 tablespoon of the oil in a large nonstick skillet over medium-low. Add the chicken and cook for 2 minutes per side, or until browned. Place the chicken on the baking sheet and bake for 10 minutes.

MEANWHILE, wipe out the skillet, add the remaining 1 tablespoon oil, and heat over medium heat. Add the onion and 1 tablespoon of the sugar. Cook until the onion is softened and lightly browned. Add the garlic and cook for a few seconds. Add the remaining 2 tablespoons flour and cook, stirring constantly, for 1 minute. Whisk in the broth, tomato paste, and remaining 1 tablespoon sugar. Season with the salt and pepper. Cook over medium heat for 5 minutes, or until thickened.

REMOVE the chicken from the oven and transfer to a serving platter. Pour the sauce over the chicken and serve.

TOTAL TIME: 20 minutes **MAKES 4 SERVINGS**

PER SERVING: 397 calories, 37 g protein, 28 g carbohydrates, 14 g total fat, 3 g saturated fat, 1 g fiber, 669 mg sodium

Brazil Nut–Crusted Oven-Fried Chicken

Brazil nuts lend a rich, nutty sweetness to the bread crumb coating in this dish. If you prefer a spicy quality, add a splash of hot sauce just before serving.

1¼ pounds chicken tenders

½ cup buttermilk

¼ cup dried bread crumbs

3 tablespoons finely chopped Brazil nuts

1 package (12 ounces) frozen kale, thawed

1 can (14.5 ounces) no-salt-added diced tomatoes

2 cloves garlic, slivered

¾ teaspoon Italian seasoning

⅛ teaspoon salt

½ cup water

PREHEAT the oven to 425°F. Line a baking sheet with parchment paper.

COMBINE the chicken and buttermilk in a medium bowl. Stir together the bread crumbs and nuts in a shallow dish or pie plate. Shake off the excess buttermilk and dip the chicken into the crumb mixture. Place on the baking sheet. Bake for 20 minutes, or until golden brown and the juices run clear.

MEANWHILE, combine the kale, tomatoes, garlic, seasoning, salt, and water in a medium saucepan over medium-high heat. Simmer for 15 minutes, or until tender. Serve with the chicken.

TOTAL TIME: 40 minutes **MAKES 4 SERVINGS**

PER SERVING: 280 calories, 38 g protein, 13 g carbohydrates, 10 g total fat, 2 g saturated fat, 3 g fiber, 290 mg sodium

Pan-Seared Chicken Tenders with Walnuts and Apples

Steamed asparagus makes an easy, vibrant side vegetable to go with this fruity main dish.

½ cup walnuts, chopped

2 teaspoons canola oil

1¼ pounds chicken tenders

1 tablespoon all-purpose flour

1 Granny Smith apple, quartered and sliced

1 small red onion, quartered and sliced

¼ teaspoon salt

¼ teaspoon ground black pepper

½ cup apple cider

TOAST the walnuts in a large nonstick skillet over medium-high heat for 5 minutes, or until fragrant. Place on a plate and set aside.

RETURN the skillet to medium-high heat and add the oil. Lightly dust the chicken with the flour on both sides. Place the chicken in the skillet. Cook for 2 to 3 minutes on one side, or until browned on the bottom. Flip and cook for 2 to 3 minutes, or until the chicken is no longer pink and the juices run clear. Transfer to a plate.

ADD the apple, onion, salt, and pepper to the skillet. Toss for 2 minutes, or until the browned bits on the bottom of the skillet are clinging to the apples. Add the cider. Bring to a boil, reduce the heat, and simmer briskly for 4 minutes, or until the cider is reduced by about half. Add the chicken and any accumulated juices on the plate and toss to coat.

DIVIDE the chicken and apple mixture among 4 plates. Sprinkle 2 tablespoons of the toasted walnuts over each serving.

TOTAL TIME: 35 minutes MAKES 4 SERVINGS

PER SERVING: 317 calories, 36 g protein, 13 g carbohydrates, 14 g total fat, 2 g saturated fat, 2 g fiber, 242 mg sodium

Braised Chicken with Tomato, Eggplant, and Olives

Japanese and Asian eggplants have a mild flavor and tender flesh. Look for the thin, straight varieties with purple, striated, or light-colored skin. Baby eggplant may be substituted.

6 ounces whole wheat penne pasta

2 tablespoons olive oil, divided

4 large plum tomatoes, chopped

2 Japanese eggplants, thinly sliced (about 4 cups)

1 onion, thinly sliced

3 cloves garlic, minced

¼ cup chopped fresh mixed herbs, such as basil and thyme

½ teaspoon salt

1 pound boneless, skinless chicken breasts or tenders, cut into 1" chunks

¼ cup pitted kalamata olives

¼ cup reduced-sodium chicken broth

PREPARE the pasta according to the package directions. Drain and stir in 1 tablespoon of the oil.

MEANWHILE, heat the remaining 1 tablespoon oil in a large skillet over medium-high heat. Add the tomatoes, eggplants, onion, garlic, herbs, and salt. Cook, stirring frequently, for 10 minutes, or until the vegetables are tender.

ADD the chicken, olives, and broth and cook for 5 minutes, or until the chicken is no longer pink and the juices run clear.

DIVIDE the pasta among 4 plates. Top with the chicken mixture.

TOTAL TIME: 30 minutes **MAKES 4 SERVINGS**

PER SERVING: 430 calories, 34 g protein, 44 g carbohydrates, 14 g total fat, 2 g saturated fat, 8 g fiber, 614 mg sodium

Rosemary Roasted Chicken and Vegetables

Double the recipe for enough to please a small dinner crowd—and since it only requires 15 minutes of prep time, you'll have time to relax before your guests arrive.

2 **small sweet potatoes (¾ pound total), peeled and cut into 1" chunks**

2 **red bell peppers, seeded and cut into ¾" chunks**

1 **sweet onion, cut into ¾" chunks, layers separated**

1 **package (10 ounces) frozen artichoke hearts**

⅛ **teaspoon salt**

¼ **teaspoon ground black pepper**

2 **teaspoons chopped fresh rosemary, divided**

½ **teaspoon olive oil, divided**

2 **boneless, skinless chicken breast halves (5 ounces each), cut in half crosswise**

1 **teaspoon grated lemon peel**

Lemon wedges

PREHEAT the oven to 425°F. Coat a roasting pan or large baking dish with cooking spray.

ARRANGE the potatoes in a shallow microwaveable bowl and microwave on high power for 2 minutes.

COMBINE the potatoes, bell peppers, onion, and artichoke hearts in the roasting pan or baking dish. Sprinkle with the salt, black pepper, 1¼ teaspoons of the rosemary, and ¼ teaspoon of the oil. Stir until combined. Move the vegetables to the sides of the pan or dish, leaving a 4" space down the center.

ARRANGE the chicken down the center of the pan or dish. Brush with the remaining ¼ teaspoon oil and sprinkle on the remaining ¾ teaspoon rosemary.

ROAST for 45 minutes, or until a thermometer inserted in the thickest portion registers 165°F and the juices run clear. Transfer the chicken to a plate. Stir the lemon peel into the roasted vegetables and serve with the chicken and lemon wedges.

TOTAL TIME: 1 hour **MAKES 4 SERVINGS**

PER SERVING: 295 calories, 19 g protein, 27 g carbohydrates, 5 g total fat, 1 g saturated fat, 8 g fiber, 196 mg sodium

Mu Shu Chicken

Here's a super-quick dish that relies on rotisserie chicken and preshredded coleslaw mix to save you time in the kitchen. Use an Asian coleslaw mix if you happen to find one in your produce department.

½ teaspoon cornstarch

1 teaspoon less-sodium soy sauce

2 tablespoons dry sherry

2 tablespoons hoisin sauce

2 teaspoons canola oil

1 tablespoon finely chopped fresh ginger

1 tablespoon minced garlic

1 bag (14 ounces) coleslaw mix

2 scallions, chopped + additional for serving

2 cups shredded rotisserie chicken breast

1 teaspoon toasted sesame oil

8 flour tortillas (6" diameter)

WHISK together the cornstarch, soy sauce, sherry, and hoisin sauce in a small bowl. Set aside.

HEAT the canola oil in a large nonstick skillet over medium-high heat. Add the ginger and garlic and cook, stirring constantly, for 1 minute.

ADD the coleslaw mix and 2 chopped scallions to the skillet and cook, stirring constantly, for 3 minutes, or until just wilted. Add the chicken and soy sauce mixture. Toss until heated through. Drizzle with the toasted sesame oil.

WARM the tortillas in the microwave oven on high power for 20 to 30 seconds. Spread the tortillas with additional hoisin sauce, if desired. Fill with the chicken mixture. Sprinkle with additional chopped scallions, if desired.

TOTAL TIME: 20 minutes **MAKES 4 SERVINGS**

PER SERVING: 328 calories, 17 g protein, 43 g carbohydrates, 10 g total fat, 2 g saturated fat, 5 g fiber, 704 mg sodium

Easy Thai Chicken

Transform a standard, store-bought rotisserie chicken into an anything-but-ordinary meal with a few flavor-packed additions. The sweet and creamy sauce uses light coconut milk instead of regular, cutting the saturated fat by nearly 60 percent.

1 cup jasmine rice, cooked

1 rotisserie chicken

1 can (13.5 ounces) light coconut milk

2 tablespoons red curry paste

4 teaspoons sugar

¼ teaspoon salt

⅛ teaspoon ground black pepper

1 cup fresh basil leaves

Lime wedges

COOK the rice according to the package directions.

MEANWHILE, pull the meat from the chicken in large pieces. Discard the skin and bones.

SPOON a few tablespoons from the top of the can of coconut milk into a medium skillet over medium-high heat. Stir in the curry paste. Add the sugar, remaining coconut milk, salt, and pepper. Bring to a simmer, add the chicken, and cook until heated through. Stir in the basil.

SERVE with the rice and lime wedges.

TOTAL TIME: 15 minutes **MAKES 4 SERVINGS**

PER SERVING: 350 calories, 31 g protein, 26 g carbohydrates, 12 g total fat, 7 g saturated fat, 1 g fiber, 836 mg sodium

Tandoori Turkey
with Curried Yogurt Sauce

The quick and tasty curry-ginger mixture does double duty as the flavoring agent for the marinade and sauce. There will be ample sauce to drizzle over both the turkey and the spinach mixture.

2 teaspoons curry powder

2 teaspoons grated fresh ginger

½ teaspoon turmeric

½ teaspoon ground cumin

⅛ teaspoon salt

4 teaspoons honey

1 teaspoon white wine vinegar

1 teaspoon + ¼ cup water

¾ cup 0% plain Greek yogurt

2 scallions, green parts only, chopped

2 tablespoons chopped fresh cilantro

1¼ pounds turkey tenders

3 cups frozen chopped broccoli

2 cups frozen leaf spinach

STIR together the curry powder, ginger, turmeric, cumin, salt, honey, vinegar, and 1 teaspoon water in a medium microwaveable bowl. Microwave on high power for 30 seconds.

PLACE 2 teaspoons of the curry mixture in a small bowl and add the yogurt, scallions, and cilantro. Stir until combined and set aside.

ADD the turkey to the remaining curry mixture in the medium bowl and toss to coat evenly. Preheat a grill or grill pan to medium heat.

MEANWHILE, combine the broccoli, spinach, and remaining ¼ cup water in a medium saucepan. Bring to a simmer, cover, and cook for 5 minutes, or until the broccoli is tender.

GRILL the turkey for 5 minutes, turning once, or until no longer pink and the juices run clear. Serve with the spinach mixture and the curried yogurt sauce.

TOTAL TIME: 30 minutes **MAKES 4 SERVINGS**

PER SERVING: 260 calories, 44 g protein, 17 g carbohydrates, 2 g total fat, 0 g saturated fat, 5 g fiber, 270 mg sodium

Turkey London Broil with Chimichurri

A turkey London broil is simply a single boneless breast of turkey, which has a shape similar to a flank steak or beef London broil. Like its beef counterpart, turkey London broil can be broiled or grilled. When served, it's typically cut thinly at an angle.

- **1** boneless, skinless turkey breast (1½ pounds)
- **3** teaspoons olive oil, divided
- **½** teaspoon ancho chili powder
- **½** teaspoon smoked paprika
- **1** cup brown rice
- **1** can (15 ounces) black beans, rinsed and drained
- **3** cloves garlic
- **¾** cup chopped fresh parsley
- **¾** cup chopped fresh cilantro
- **½** cup water
- **3** tablespoons fresh lime juice
- **1** tablespoon sliced pickled jalapeño chile pepper
- **¾** teaspoon dried oregano
- **½** teaspoon salt

PREHEAT the oven to 350°F.

PLACE the turkey in a roasting pan. Drizzle the turkey with 1 teaspoon of the oil and rub to coat. Sprinkle with the chili powder and paprika, and rub over the turkey until evenly coated.

BAKE for 50 to 60 minutes, or until a thermometer inserted in the thickest portion registers 170°F and the juices run clear. Let stand for 5 minutes.

MEANWHILE, prepare the rice according to the package directions. Remove from the heat and stir in the beans.

PROCESS the garlic in a blender or food processor until finely chopped. Add the parsley and cilantro and process until finely chopped. Add the water, lime juice, jalapeño, oregano, salt, and remaining 2 teaspoons oil. Process until blended.

SERVE the turkey drizzled with the sauce along with the rice and beans.

TOTAL TIME: 1 hour 10 minutes **MAKES 4 SERVINGS**

PER SERVING: 326 calories, 34 g protein, 35 g carbohydrates, 5 g total fat, 1 g saturated fat, 5 g fiber, 488 mg sodium

Turkey Croquettes

Using a broiler instead of a deep fryer slashes the calories in this dish. Lingonberry jam is a staple food in Scandinavian cuisine, but if you happen to prepare this recipe with Thanksgiving leftovers, then cranberry sauce would be a natural substitute.

- 2 tablespoons olive oil
- 1 tablespoon unsalted butter
- 1 shallot, finely chopped
- ¼ cup all-purpose flour
- ¾ cup buttermilk
- 2 teaspoons fresh lemon juice
- 2 teaspoons dried thyme
- 2½ cups finely chopped cooked turkey
- 1¼ cups soft whole wheat bread crumbs
- 1 cup lingonberry jam

HEAT the oil and butter in a saucepan over medium heat. Add the shallot and cook for 2 minutes.

ADD the flour and cook, whisking constantly, for 2 minutes. Gradually add the buttermilk, lemon juice, and thyme, whisking for 1 minute, or until well combined and thickened. Transfer to a large bowl.

STIR in the turkey. With wet hands, shape the mixture into 18 ovals (1 tablespoon each). Coat in the bread crumbs and place on an oiled baking sheet.

PREHEAT the broiler. Broil the croquettes 6" from the heat for 5 minutes, turning if needed, or until golden brown. Serve with the jam.

TOTAL TIME: 30 minutes **MAKES 6 SERVINGS**

PER SERVING: 289 calories, 19 g protein, 34 g carbohydrates, 4 g total fat, 3 g saturated fat, 2 g fiber, 104 mg sodium

Rotini with Broccoli and Turkey

If rotini isn't your favorite pasta, you can use another type in its place. Just be sure to choose one with a shape that will hold onto the chunky ingredients in this dish.

- 8 ounces multigrain rotini pasta
- 2 tablespoons olive oil
- 1 pound broccoli crowns, cut into bite-size florets
- 2 cloves garlic, minced
- 2 tablespoons water
- ¼ teaspoon red-pepper flakes
- 2 cups chopped cooked turkey breast
- ¼ cup grated Parmesan cheese

BRING a large pot of salted water to a boil. Cook the pasta according to the package directions.

MEANWHILE, heat the oil in a large nonstick skillet over medium heat. Add the broccoli, garlic, water, and red-pepper flakes. Cook, covered, for 5 minutes, or until the broccoli is tender-crisp. Add the turkey and toss to combine. Remove from the heat.

DRAIN the pasta, reserving ½ cup of the cooking liquid. Add the pasta to the skillet with the broccoli and turkey. Stir in the reserved cooking liquid, if necessary, to loosen the mixture. Divide among 4 bowls and top with the grated cheese.

TOTAL TIME: 25 minutes **MAKES 4 SERVINGS**

PER SERVING: 402 calories, 36 g protein, 43 g carbohydrates, 10 g total fat, 2 g saturated fat, 6 g fiber, 158 mg sodium

WHY YOU SHOULD CHOOSE

Whole grain pasta

Whole grain pasta is relatively quick to prepare, with even the longest-cooking shapes taking less than 20 minutes. Although many people think couscous is a type of grain, it actually is very fine nuggets of pasta.

Meat

CHAPTER
13

Greek-Seasoned Filet of Beef with Cucumber Tzatziki

For a salad variation, slice the steaks and serve with tomato and lettuce instead of the broccoli.

4 beef filet steaks
(about 4 ounces each)

2 tablespoons lemon juice

1 teaspoon dried oregano

2 cloves garlic, minced
and divided

1 cup 0% plain Greek yogurt

1 cucumber, peeled, seeded,
grated, and excess liquid
squeezed out

6 cups broccoli florets

⅛ teaspoon salt

⅛ teaspoon ground
black pepper

4 small whole wheat pitas
(4" diameter), toasted

COMBINE the steaks, lemon juice, oregano, and half of the garlic in a bowl. Turn to coat and let stand for 10 minutes.

MEANWHILE, to make the tzatziki, combine the yogurt, cucumber, and remaining garlic in a small bowl. Set aside.

PLACE a steamer basket in a large saucepan with 2" of water. Bring to a boil over high heat. Steam the broccoli in the basket for 4 minutes, or until tender-crisp. Remove from the heat and keep warm.

REMOVE the steaks from the marinade and discard marinade. Sprinkle the steaks with the salt and pepper. Coat a nonstick grill pan with cooking spray and heat over medium-high heat. Cook the steaks for 8 minutes, turning once, or until a thermometer inserted in the center registers 145°F for medium-rare, 160°F for medium, or 165°F for well-done. Let stand for 10 minutes before serving.

SERVE each steak with ¼ cup cucumber tzatziki, 1½ cups broccoli, and 1 pita.

TOTAL TIME: 25 minutes **MAKES 4 SERVINGS**

PER SERVING: 325 calories, 36 g protein, 26 g carbohydrates, 9 g total fat, 3 g saturated fat, 6 g fiber, 337 mg sodium

Marinated Broiled Flank Steak with Sweet-and-Sour Beet Greens

This highly flavorful but simple marinade also works wonderfully on boneless, skinless chicken breasts or thighs and pork.

1 **pound flank steak, trimmed of all visible fat**

1 **large shallot, finely chopped**

3 **cloves garlic, minced**

1 **teaspoon chopped fresh thyme**

1 **teaspoon olive oil**

4 **tablespoons balsamic vinegar, divided**

⅛ **teaspoon salt**

⅛ **teaspoon ground black pepper**

1 **cup uncooked couscous**

10 **cups beet greens, washed, chopped, and left damp**

1 **tablespoon sugar**

2 **teaspoons grated lemon peel**

COMBINE the steak, shallot, garlic, thyme, oil, and 3 tablespoons of the vinegar in a resealable plastic bag. Seal, turn several times to coat the steak, and refrigerate for 1 to 24 hours, turning occasionally.

PREHEAT the broiler. Coat a broiler-pan rack with cooking spray.

REMOVE the steak from the bag and wipe off the excess marinade. Sprinkle the steak with salt and pepper. Broil 5" from the heat for 10 minutes, turning once, or until a thermometer inserted in the center registers 145°F for medium-rare, 160°F for medium, or 165°F for well-done. Let stand for 10 minutes before thinly slicing across the grain.

COOK the couscous according to the package directions.

MEANWHILE, heat a large nonstick skillet coated with cooking spray over medium-high heat. Add the greens and cook, stirring often, for 2 minutes, or until starting to wilt. Add the sugar and remaining 1 tablespoon vinegar and cook, stirring constantly, for 2 minutes, or until wilted. Remove from the heat and stir in the lemon peel. Divide the steak, greens, and couscous among 4 plates.

TOTAL TIME: 30 minutes + marinating time **MAKES 4 SERVINGS**

PER SERVING: 313 calories, 30 g protein, 30 g carbohydrates, 8 g total fat, 3 g saturated fat, 4 g fiber, 316 mg sodium

Grilled Flank Steak with Chimichurri

Chimichurri is a bright herbal sauce that's popular in Argentina—and it may well be one of the best accompaniments for grilled steak.

- 3 tablespoons red wine vinegar
- 2 tablespoons water
- 3 cloves garlic, minced
- ¾ teaspoon salt, divided
- ½ teaspoon red-pepper flakes
- ¾ teaspoon coarsely ground black pepper, divided
- ¼ cup olive oil
- ½ cup finely chopped fresh flat-leaf parsley
- 1 pound flank, skirt, or sirloin steak, trimmed of all visible fat
- 1 bunch scallions

MAKE the chimichurri sauce by combining the vinegar, water, garlic, ½ teaspoon of the salt, the red-pepper flakes, and ½ teaspoon of the black pepper in a small bowl. Whisk in the oil until combined. Whisk in the parsley.

PREHEAT a grill or grill pan to high heat. Season the steak with the remaining ¼ teaspoon salt and remaining ¼ teaspoon pepper. Grill for 3 to 4 minutes per side, or until a thermometer inserted in the center registers 145°F for medium-rare. Trim the roots from the scallions and add the entire bunch to the grill just after turning the steak. Cook the scallions for 4 to 5 minutes, or until lightly charred.

LET the steak stand for 10 minutes before serving. Drizzle with the chimichurri and serve with the grilled scallions.

TOTAL TIME: 20 minutes **MAKES 4 SERVINGS**

PER SERVING: 561 calories, 38 g protein, 8 g carbohydrates, 41 g total fat, 10 g saturated fat, 3 g fiber, 261 mg sodium

Penne with Pepper Steak and Caramelized Onions

Caramelizing is a process that brings out the deep, rich sweetness from the natural sugars in onions as they cook. Heat also triggers chemical reactions that increase the variety of the beneficial sulfur-containing compounds found in onions.

¾ pound flank steak, trimmed of all visible fat

2 tablespoons cracked black pepper

2 cloves garlic, minced

1 tablespoon canola oil

1 large yellow onion, sliced

1 red onion, sliced

2 tablespoons balsamic vinegar

1 cup reduced-sodium beef broth

8 ounces multigrain penne pasta

1 bag (6 ounces) baby arugula

Shaved Parmesan cheese

PREHEAT the broiler. Place the flank steak on the rack of a broiler pan and coat on all sides with the pepper and garlic. Let stand for about 10 minutes.

HEAT the oil in a large skillet over medium-high heat. Cook the onions for 8 minutes, or until lightly browned. Reduce the heat to medium-low and add the vinegar to deglaze the skillet, scraping up the browned bits with a wooden spoon. Stir in the broth, cover, and cook for 15 minutes, or until the onions are very soft and browned. Remove from the heat.

PREPARE the pasta according to the package directions, drain, and place in a large bowl.

MEANWHILE, broil the steak 4" from the heat for 12 minutes, or until a thermometer inserted in the center registers 145°F for medium-rare, 160°F for medium, or 165°F for well-done. Let stand for 10 minutes before thinly slicing across the grain.

STIR the arugula into the onions. Add to the pasta and toss to coat. Add the steak and top with the cheese.

TOTAL TIME: 1 hour 10 minutes **MAKES 4 SERVINGS**

PER SERVING: 435 calories, 28 g protein, 54 g carbohydrates, 12 g total fat, 3 g saturated fat, 8 g fiber, 185 mg sodium

Broiled Beef Kebabs

The instructions here are for indoor broiling, but this dish is perfect for outdoor grilling, too. If you want to add a little more variety to the finished meal, add some cremini mushrooms and red onions to the kebabs. The extra calories from the vegetables will be marginal.

1 pound beef sirloin, cut into 24 pieces

1 tablespoon olive oil

2 cloves garlic, minced

¼ teaspoon salt

⅛ teaspoon ground black pepper

2 zucchini, sliced

2 cups grape tomatoes

2 tablespoons chopped fresh basil (optional)

SOAK 8 bamboo skewers in water for 30 minutes. Meanwhile, toss the beef, oil, and garlic in a large bowl. Season with the salt and pepper.

PREHEAT the broiler. Thread the beef, zucchini, and tomatoes alternately onto the skewers. Arrange on the rack of a broiler pan.

BROIL for 2 to 3 minutes per side, or until the beef is the desired doneness and the vegetables are tender. Remove from the oven. Cover loosely with foil and let stand for 5 minutes before removing from the skewers. Stir the basil, if using, into the vegetable mixture.

TOTAL TIME: 50 minutes **MAKES 4 SERVINGS**

PER SERVING: 211 calories, 27 g protein, 7 g carbohydrates, 8 g total fat, 2 g saturated fat, 2 g fiber, 148 mg sodium

Beef and Eggplant Tagine

In Moroccan cuisine, tagines are braised meat dishes that are fragrant with spices. This version has the same flavors, but it uses ground beef so it doesn't require a long cooking time.

¾ pound extra-lean ground beef

½ tablespoon olive oil

1 eggplant, peeled and cut into 1" cubes

2 small yellow squash, cut into quarter rounds

4 cloves garlic, smashed

1 tablespoon slivered fresh ginger

1 teaspoon garam masala

½ teaspoon ground cinnamon

1 can (14.5 ounces) diced tomatoes with basil and oregano

½ cup small pitted black olives, halved

½ cup canned chickpeas, rinsed and drained

⅛ teaspoon salt

1 tablespoon mild hot sauce

1 cup whole wheat couscous

2 tablespoons chopped pistachios

HEAT a large nonstick saucepan or deep skillet coated with cooking spray over medium-high heat. Add the beef and cook, breaking it up with a wooden spoon, for 6 to 8 minutes, or until no longer pink. Transfer to a bowl and set aside.

HEAT the oil in the same saucepan or skillet. Add the eggplant and cook for 5 minutes, stirring occasionally. Add the squash, garlic, ginger, garam masala, and cinnamon. Cook, stirring frequently, for 1 minute, or until the spices are fragrant and toasted.

ADD the tomatoes, olives, chickpeas, salt, and beef. Bring to a simmer and cook, covered, for 10 minutes, or until the vegetables are tender. Remove from the heat and stir in the hot sauce.

MEANWHILE, prepare the couscous according to the package directions. Serve the tagine with the couscous and sprinkle with the pistachios.

TOTAL TIME: 45 minutes **MAKES 4 SERVINGS**

PER SERVING: 380 calories, 27 g protein, 40 g carbohydrates, 12 g total fat, 3 g saturated fat, 9 g fiber, 679 mg sodium

Korean Beef in Lettuce Leaves

Folded into crisp lettuce leaves, these savory beef bundles are ideal for a summer evening meal. If you prefer poultry instead of beef, the bundles are just as easy to prepare with lean ground turkey.

3 tablespoons 100% fruit orange marmalade

2 tablespoons reduced-sodium soy sauce

1 tablespoon hoisin sauce

1 tablespoon grated fresh ginger

1 clove garlic, minced

2 tablespoons canola oil

1 pound extra-lean ground beef

8 scallions, sliced

2 carrots, finely chopped

1 red bell pepper, seeded and finely chopped

12 leaves Boston or Bibb lettuce

WHISK together the marmalade, soy sauce, hoisin sauce, ginger, and garlic in a small bowl. Set aside.

HEAT the oil in a large skillet over medium-high heat. Cook the beef, scallions, carrots, and pepper, stirring often, for 5 to 7 minutes, or until the beef is no longer pink. Add the soy sauce mixture and cook, stirring often, for 5 minutes, or until well blended.

SPOON the beef mixture into the lettuce leaves and serve.

TOTAL TIME: 30 minutes **MAKES 4 SERVINGS**

PER SERVING: 317 calories, 26 g protein, 18 g carbohydrates, 16 g total fat, 4 g saturated fat, 3 g fiber, 453 mg sodium

Beef Tacos with Cilantro Cream

Fill the tacos and serve with mounds of lettuce and chopped fresh tomatoes. There will be ample sauce to dress the leftover salad ingredients.

¼ cup fat-free plain yogurt

¼ cup reduced-fat sour cream

3 tablespoons chopped fresh cilantro

¼ teaspoon salt, divided

1 pound extra-lean ground beef

1 small onion, finely chopped

2 teaspoons chili powder

1 teaspoon ground cumin

½ cup canned no-salt-added tomato puree

2 tablespoons ketchup

8 hard taco shells

4 cups shredded iceberg lettuce

2 tomatoes, chopped

Lime wedges

STIR together the yogurt, sour cream, cilantro, and a pinch of the salt in a small bowl. Set aside.

COMBINE the beef, onion, chili powder, cumin, and remaining salt in a nonstick skillet over medium-high heat. Cook, breaking up the beef with a wooden spoon, for 7 minutes, or until no longer pink. Add the tomato puree and ketchup. Cook the beef mixture for 2 minutes longer, or until thickened.

SPOON the beef mixture into the taco shells and serve with the lettuce, tomatoes, lime wedges, and cilantro cream.

TOTAL TIME: 30 minutes **MAKES 8**

PER SERVING (2 TACOS): 332 calories, 29 g protein, 27 g carbohydrates, 12 g total fat, 6 g saturated fat, 4 g fiber, 343 mg sodium

Greek Meatballs

This easy one-dish meal is a real time-saver because it can be prepared and refrigerated for up to 24 hours before baking. Prepare ¾ cup of brown rice to yield 2 cups cooked rice for this recipe.

2 cups cooked brown rice, cooled

¾ teaspoon dried oregano

4 tablespoons (1 ounce) reduced-fat crumbled feta cheese, divided

1 pound extra-lean ground beef

2 zucchini (1 pound total), cut into thin slices

1 cup bottled marinara sauce

PREHEAT the oven to 450°F. Coat a 13" × 9" baking dish with cooking spray.

COMBINE the rice, oregano, and 2 tablespoons of the cheese in a large bowl. Stir in the beef until combined.

SCATTER the zucchini in a single layer in the baking dish. Shape the meat mixture into sixteen 1½" balls using a small ice cream scoop. Arrange the meatballs over the zucchini. Drizzle with the marinara sauce. Cover with foil.

BAKE for 22 minutes, or until the meatballs are no longer pink inside.

UNCOVER and top with the remaining 2 tablespoons cheese. Let stand in the oven for 1 minute, or until the cheese melts slightly.

TOTAL TIME: 35 minutes **MAKES 4 SERVINGS**

PER SERVING: 337 calories, 30 g protein, 32 g carbohydrates, 10 g total fat, 4 g saturated fat, 4 g fiber, 428 mg sodium

Pasta Bolognese

The Italians traditionally make Bolognese with pork, veal, and beef—a rich combination that makes for a delicious but calorie-laden bowl that is further enhanced with wine and milk or cream. In this recipe, dried mushrooms and fat-free ricotta work their magic to render this dish substantially lower in calories.

5 dried porcini mushrooms

1 heaping cup rotini, small shells, or ziti pasta

½ pound extra-lean ground beef

1 tablespoon finely chopped yellow onion

1 teaspoon chili powder

1 teaspoon dried basil

Pinch of ground black pepper

1 can (8 ounces) tomato sauce

2 tablespoons fat-free ricotta cheese

BRING 4 quarts of water to a boil in a large pot over high heat. Add the mushrooms and pasta. Cook for 10 to 12 minutes, or until the pasta is al dente.

MEANWHILE, heat a large nonstick skillet over medium-high heat. Add the beef, onion, chili powder, basil, and pepper. Cook, breaking up the beef with a wooden spoon, for 6 to 8 minutes, or until the beef is no longer pink. Add the tomato sauce. Bring to a boil. Pour into a large bowl. Stir in the ricotta.

DRAIN the pasta and mushrooms. Add to the sauce and toss to combine.

TOTAL TIME: 35 minutes   **MAKES 2 SERVINGS**

PER SERVING: 365 calories, 39 g protein, 33 g carbohydrates, 8 g total fat, 3 g saturated fat, 3 g fiber, 683 mg sodium

Stuffed Red Peppers

Splitting the peppers lengthwise allows you to keep the stem attached. For a more festive look, use yellow, orange, red, and green peppers and allow everyone to mix and match a color combination that suits their taste.

4 **large red bell peppers, halved lengthwise and seeded**

1 **tablespoon olive oil**

1 **pound extra-lean ground beef**

1 **onion, chopped**

8 **ounces cremini mushrooms, chopped**

2 **cups fresh spinach**

¼ **teaspoon salt**

¼ **teaspoon ground black pepper**

1 **cup shredded reduced-fat mozzarella cheese**

2 **tablespoons chopped fresh parsley**

PREHEAT the oven to 450°F. Coat a 13" × 9" baking dish with cooking spray. Arrange the bell peppers, cut sides up, in the baking dish.

HEAT the oil in a large nonstick skillet over medium-high heat. Add the beef and cook, breaking it up with a wooden spoon, for 6 to 8 minutes, or until no longer pink. Add the onion and mushrooms and cook for 5 minutes, or until the vegetables soften. Add the spinach and cook for 1 minute, or until wilted. Season with the salt and black pepper.

FILL the bell peppers with the beef mixture. Top with the cheese. Cover with foil.

BAKE for 20 minutes, or until the bell peppers are tender and the cheese melts. Sprinkle with the parsley before serving.

TOTAL TIME: 45 minutes **MAKES 4 SERVINGS**

PER SERVING: 336 calories, 35 g protein, 16 g carbohydrates, 14 g total fat, 6 g saturated fat, 5 g fiber, 346 mg sodium

Shepherd's Pie

Warm up a winter night with this variation of shepherd's pie. Store-bought (or leftover) mashed potatoes are a simple shortcut. Then give the dish a pop of smoky heat with ground chipotle chile pepper.

1 teaspoon canola oil

1 pound extra-lean ground beef

1 teaspoon ground chipotle chile pepper (or 1 tablespoon chili powder)

⅛ teaspoon ground black pepper

1 package (10 ounces) frozen sweet corn, thawed

1 can (11 ounces) Mexican-style whole kernel corn, drained

2½ cups prepared mashed potatoes

PREHEAT the oven to 375°F.

HEAT the oil in a large nonstick skillet over medium-high heat. Add the beef and cook, breaking it up with a wooden spoon, for 6 to 8 minutes, or until no longer pink. Season with the chipotle chile pepper (or chili powder) and black pepper.

STIR in the cream-style corn and Mexican-style corn. Transfer the mixture into an 8" × 8" baking dish. Spread the mashed potatoes over the top. Bake for 15 to 20 minutes, or until bubbly around the edges. Change the oven temperature to broil. Broil for 2 to 3 minutes to brown the top.

TOTAL TIME: 30 minutes **MAKES 4 SERVINGS**

PER SERVING: 372 calories, 30 g protein, 47 g carbohydrates, 8 g total fat, 3 g saturated fat, 5 g fiber, 664 mg sodium

Beef Goulash Noodle Casserole

Baking this casserole in the oven allows you to leave it unattended, but if you prefer a stove-top dish, just keep the lid on tight and turn the heat down to low.

- 2 tablespoons canola oil
- 1 onion, chopped
- ½ red bell pepper, seeded and chopped
- 1¼ teaspoons paprika
- 1 teaspoon dried thyme
- ¾ pound extra-lean ground beef
- 1 can (14.5 ounces) no-salt-added petite diced tomatoes
- 3 ounces dried, wide whole wheat egg noodles
- ½ cup fat-free low-sodium beef or vegetable broth
- ½ teaspoon ground black pepper
- ¼ teaspoon salt
- ¼ cup fat-free sour cream
- 1½ tablespoons all-purpose flour

PREHEAT the oven to 350°F.

HEAT the oil in a Dutch oven over medium-high heat. Add the onion, bell pepper, paprika, and thyme. Cook, stirring occasionally, for 3 minutes.

CRUMBLE the beef into the pan. Cook, stirring occasionally, for 4 minutes, or until the beef is no longer pink. Stir in the tomatoes, noodles, broth, black pepper, and salt.

COVER tightly and bake for 15 minutes. Carefully remove the cover and stir. Bake, uncovered, for 10 minutes. Remove from the oven, cover, and let stand for 10 minutes, or until the noodles are tender.

MEANWHILE, whisk together the sour cream and flour in a small bowl. Whisk into the casserole. Stir over low heat for 1 to 2 minutes, or until thickened.

TOTAL TIME: 55 minutes **MAKES 4 SERVINGS**

PER SERVING: 330 calories, 24 g protein, 30 g carbohydrates, 12 g total fat, 3 g saturated fat, 3 g fiber, 250 mg sodium

Linguine with Braised Kale, Garlic, and Sausage

Braising the sausage along with the kale allows its flavor to permeate the whole dish.

6 ounces linguine

1 teaspoon olive oil

6 ounces sweet Italian sausage, removed from the casings

6 cups chopped kale

4 cloves garlic, sliced

1 cup low-sodium chicken broth, divided

2 plum tomatoes, seeded and chopped

¼ cup fresh basil leaves, sliced

2 teaspoons grated Parmesan cheese

Red-pepper flakes (optional)

PREPARE the linguine according to the package directions.

MEANWHILE, heat the oil in a large nonstick skillet over medium-high heat. Cook the sausage, breaking it up with a wooden spoon, for 5 minutes, or until no longer pink. Stir in the kale and garlic. Cook for 2 minutes, or until the kale starts to wilt. Add ½ cup of the broth. Reduce the heat to medium-low, cover, and simmer for 5 minutes.

INCREASE the heat to medium-high, uncover, and add the tomatoes and remaining ½ cup broth. Cook for 5 minutes.

STIR in the linguine and cook for 1 minute, tossing occasionally, or until heated through. Stir in the basil. Divide among 4 bowls and sprinkle each with ½ teaspoon of the cheese and some red-pepper flakes, if using.

TOTAL TIME: 30 minutes **MAKES 4 SERVINGS**

PER SERVING: 296 calories, 17 g protein, 45 g carbohydrates, 6 g total fat, 2 g saturated fat, 4 g fiber, 320 mg sodium

Honey-Glazed Pork Dinner

Roasted pork, garlicky mashed potatoes, and perfectly roasted broccoli are a snap to prepare with these easy instructions.

½ cup apple juice

2 tablespoons honey

1 tablespoon reduced-sodium soy sauce

¼ teaspoon ground red pepper

4 cloves garlic, minced and divided

1½ pounds pork tenderloin, trimmed of all visible fat

4 cups broccoli florets

2 tablespoons olive oil, divided

½ teaspoon salt, divided

1½ pounds Yukon gold potatoes, peeled and quartered

½ cup reduced-fat sour cream

¼ cup chopped parsley

PREHEAT the oven to 400°F. Combine the juice, honey, soy sauce, red pepper, and half of the garlic in a small bowl.

TOSS the broccoli with 1 tablespoon of the oil on a rimmed baking sheet. Sprinkle with ¼ teaspoon of the salt.

HEAT the remaining 1 tablespoon oil in a medium ovenproof skillet over high heat. Add the pork and cook for 8 minutes, turning once, or until browned. Remove from the heat. Pour the juice mixture over the pork and transfer to the oven along with the pan of broccoli.

BAKE the pork and broccoli for 25 to 30 minutes, or until a thermometer inserted in the center of the pork registers 160°F and the juices run clear.

MEANWHILE, place the potatoes in a medium pot and cover with cold water. Bring to a boil over high heat and cook for 20 to 25 minutes, or until tender. Drain the potatoes and return to the pot. Add the sour cream, parsley, remaining ¼ teaspoon salt, and remaining garlic. Mash until smooth.

TRANSFER the pork to a cutting board. Return the skillet to high heat and cook the juice mixture for 3 to 4 minutes, or until a thick glaze forms. Remove from the heat. Slice the pork and arrange on a plate. Drizzle with the glaze and serve with the mashed potatoes and broccoli.

TOTAL TIME: 55 minutes **MAKES 4 SERVINGS**

PER SERVING: 503 calories, 43 g protein, 49 g carbohydrates, 15 g total fat, 4.5 g saturated fat, 5 g fiber, 560 mg sodium

Pork Chops
with Sweet-and-Sour Cabbage

Its bright flavors and cheerful colors make this dish a perfect midwinter meal.

1 tablespoon olive oil

4 boneless pork chops
(4 ounces each)

1 pound shredded
red cabbage

1 large red onion, sliced

2 tablespoons firmly packed
brown sugar

¼ cup balsamic vinegar

HEAT the oil in a large skillet over medium-high heat. Add the pork and cook for 3 to 5 minutes per side, or until a thermometer inserted in the center registers 160°F and the juices run clear. Transfer the pork to a plate and cover loosely to keep warm.

COMBINE the cabbage, onion, and sugar in the same skillet. Reduce the heat to medium and cook for 10 minutes, or until tender.

ADD the vinegar and cook for 1 minute longer. Serve the cabbage with the pork chops.

TOTAL TIME: 25 minutes **MAKES 4 SERVINGS**

PER SERVING: 293 calories, 27 g protein, 21 g carbohydrates, 11 g total fat, 3 g saturated fat, 3 g fiber, 89 mg sodium

Asparagus, Red Pepper, and Pork Stir-Fry over Quinoa

Quinoa is a great substitute for rice. It is high in protein and has a pleasantly light texture.

⅔ cup quinoa, rinsed

1⅓ cups water

1 pound pork tenderloin, trimmed of all visible fat and cut into ¾" chunks

2 tablespoons reduced-sodium soy sauce, divided

2 tablespoons hoisin sauce

3 teaspoons toasted sesame oil, divided

1 onion, chopped

2 cloves garlic, minced

1 tablespoon grated fresh ginger

1 red bell pepper, cut into thin strips

¾ pound asparagus, cut into 2" pieces

4 scallions, cut into 1" pieces

BRING the quinoa and water to a boil in a small saucepan over medium-high heat. Reduce the heat to medium, cover, and simmer for 20 minutes, or until the liquid is absorbed and the quinoa is tender. Remove from the heat and keep warm.

MEANWHILE, combine the pork and 1 tablespoon of the soy sauce in a medium bowl, tossing to coat well. Combine the hoisin sauce and the remaining 1 tablespoon soy sauce in a small bowl and set aside.

HEAT 1 teaspoon of the oil in a large nonstick skillet over medium-high heat. Cook the pork, stirring occasionally, for 5 minutes, or until lightly browned. Transfer to a plate.

HEAT the remaining 2 teaspoons oil in the same skillet over medium-high heat. Add the onion, garlic, and ginger and cook for 1 minute, stirring often. Add the bell pepper and asparagus. Cook, stirring occasionally, for 3 minutes, or until tender-crisp.

STIR in the scallions, hoisin sauce mixture, and pork with any juices that have accumulated. Cook for 1 minute, or until heated through. Serve over the quinoa.

TOTAL TIME: 40 minutes **MAKES 4 SERVINGS**

PER SERVING: 315 calories, 25 g protein, 33 g carbohydrates, 10 g total fat, 2 g saturated fat, 5 g fiber, 282 mg sodium

Desserts

CHAPTER
14

301

Perfect Dessert Parfaits

Ripen mangoes in a paper bag at room temperature. Once ripe, store them in a plastic bag in the refrigerator for up to 5 days.

2 cups chopped pineapple

2 cups chopped mango

2 tablespoons fresh lime juice

4 cups 0% vanilla Greek yogurt

¼ cup chopped pecans

COMBINE the pineapple, mango, and lime juice in a medium bowl.

PLACE ⅓ cup of the yogurt in the bottom of each of 4 small glasses. Divide one-third of the fruit mixture and one-third of the pecans among the glasses. Repeat the layers 2 more times with the remaining yogurt, fruit mixture, and pecans.

TOTAL TIME: 10 minutes **MAKES 4**

PER PARFAIT: 276 calories, 24 g protein, 34 g carbohydrates, 5 g total fat, 0.5 g saturated fat, 3 g fiber, 93 mg sodium

Fruit Kebabs
with Raspberry-Mango Dip

This dip can be made and refrigerated up to 3 days before use. You can use frozen raspberries instead of fresh. To save time, purchase precut cantaloupe, pineapple, and watermelon from the grocery store.

1 **mango, cut into chunks**

½ **cup raspberries**

¼ **cup 0% plain Greek yogurt**

2 **tablespoons honey**

1½ **cups strawberries,**
    halved if large

1 **banana, cut into 1" chunks**

1 **cup cubed cantaloupe**

1 **cup cubed pineapple**

1 **cup cubed watermelon**

½ **cup green or red grapes**

¼ **cup almonds**

PROCESS the mango in a food processor until smooth. Add the raspberries, yogurt, and honey. Process until smooth. Pour into a small bowl. Cover and refrigerate while assembling the kebabs.

THREAD the strawberries, banana, cantaloupe, pineapple, watermelon, and grapes onto eight 8" wooden skewers. Serve 2 kebabs per person, with the dip and almonds.

TOTAL TIME: 20 minutes **MAKES 4 SERVINGS**

PER SERVING: 233 calories, 5 g protein, 47 g carbohydrates, 5 g total fat, 1 g saturated fat, 6 g fiber, 16 mg sodium

Apple Slices with Spiced Ricotta Dip

Ricotta cheese can sometimes have a grainy quality, so here it's paired with just a bit of smooth peanut butter to even out the texture.

½ **cup fat-free ricotta cheese**

1½ **teaspoons smooth peanut butter**

Pinch of ground cinnamon

1 **small apple, cored and sliced**

STIR together the ricotta, peanut butter, and cinnamon in a small bowl until smooth. Serve the dip with the apple slices.

TOTAL TIME: 5 minutes **MAKES 1 SERVING**

PER SERVING: 225 calories, 12 g protein, 32 g carbohydrates, 4 g total fat, 1 g saturated fat, 4 g fiber, 168 mg sodium

Seasonings from Around the World

Stock up on seasonings and spices that add flavor without calories. A well-stocked spice drawer is essential. It also is handy for creating your own dishes or modifying ours with seasonings from other regions. Here's a list of typical seasonings to help you get started.

CUISINE	TYPICAL SEASONINGS
French	Bay leaf, tarragon, thyme
Spanish	Paprika, saffron, smoked paprika
North African	Cinnamon, cardamom, chile pepper, cumin, turmeric, ginger, nutmeg, za'atar
Caribbean	Allspice, nutmeg, chile pepper, cinnamon, curry powder, ginger
Mexican	Chile pepper, cinnamon, oregano, allspice, cumin
Indian	Curry powder, cardamom, cinnamon, coriander seeds, cumin, fennel seeds, mustard, turmeric
Chinese	Chile pepper, cinnamon, five-spice powder, star anise

Maria's Rhubarb Sauce with Strawberries

Rhubarb is a member of the buckwheat family, and its thick, celery-like stalks can reach up to 2 feet in length. They're the only edible portion of the plant—the leaves are considered toxic.

10 stalks rhubarb (about 1¼ pounds total), cut into 1" pieces

½ cup water

1 cup sugar

¼ teaspoon ground cloves

2 pounds strawberries, hulled and quartered

COMBINE the rhubarb and water in a medium heavy-bottom saucepan and bring to a boil over medium heat.

ADD the sugar and cloves. Cook for 20 minutes, or until the rhubarb is reduced to a sauce. Serve over the strawberries.

TOTAL TIME: 30 minutes **MAKES 8 SERVINGS**

PER SERVING: 147 calories, 1 g protein, 37 g carbohydrates, 1 g total fat, 0 g saturated fat, 3 g fiber, 5 mg sodium

Homemade Fruity Yogurt Pops

Tangy and sweet, these easy-to-make treats are better and less expensive than their store-bought counterparts. If you don't have ice-pop molds, just use 4-ounce paper cups and then peel them off when ready to eat.

1½ large mangoes,
   cut into chunks

2 cups fat-free plain yogurt

½ cup sugar

½ cup fat-free milk

COMBINE the mangoes, yogurt, sugar, and milk in a blender and pulse until smooth. Pour the mixture into eight 4-ounce ice-pop molds. Insert a wooden stick into each and freeze for 6 hours. Unmold before serving.

TOTAL TIME: 10 minutes + freezing time **MAKES 8**

PER POP: 113 calories, 4 g protein, 25 g carbohydrates, 0 g total fat, 0 g saturated fat, 1 g fiber, 54 mg sodium

Blackberry Dessert

Use fresh blackberries in this dish if you can and reserve a few for the garnish. Of course, if this lush berry happens to be out of season, the frozen version will work fine, too.

¼ cup sugar

1½ teaspoons cornstarch

¾ pound blackberries

8 small shortbread cookies, crumbled

COMBINE the sugar and cornstarch in a medium heavy-bottom saucepan. Add the blackberries and mash a few times. Bring to a boil over medium-high heat, stirring occasionally. Remove from the heat and let cool slightly.

DIVIDE the blackberry mixture among 4 dishes. Top with the crumbled shortbread cookies.

TOTAL TIME: 10 minutes **MAKES 4 SERVINGS**

PER SERVING: 159 calories, 2 g protein, 31 g carbohydrates, 4 g total fat, 1 g saturated fat, 4 g fiber, 66 mg sodium

WHY YOU SHOULD CHOOSE

Frozen and fresh berries

Packed with vitamin C and fiber and relatively low in calories, berries brighten up breakfast, dessert, or a smoothie. Frozen berries are a perfect alternative when fresh are not available.

Grilled Peaches with Macaroons and Caramel Sauce

//

Grilling enhances the natural sugar found in this healthy summer fruit, and a drizzle of caramel makes it decadently delicious.

4 peaches, halved and pitted

4 coconut macaroons

¼ cup jarred caramel topping

COAT a grill rack with cooking spray. Preheat the grill to medium heat.

GRILL the peaches, cut sides down, for 10 minutes, turning once, or until lightly browned and tender.

ARRANGE 2 peach halves on each of 4 dessert plates and crumble the macaroons into the cavities and over the tops. Spoon the caramel topping evenly over each serving.

//

TOTAL TIME: 15 minutes **MAKES 4 SERVINGS**

PER SERVING: 209 calories, 2 g protein, 46 g carbohydrates, 4 g total fat, 3 g saturated fat, 3 g fiber, 131 mg sodium

Butterscotch Pudding with Bananas

For a twist, melt 1 teaspoon of margarine in a medium nonstick skillet over medium heat. Add the sliced banana and 1 teaspoon of sugar and cook for 5 minutes, or until the banana is softened and warm. Then spoon over the puddings just before serving.

2¼ cups fat-free milk, divided

2 egg yolks

½ cup firmly packed light brown sugar

3 tablespoons cornstarch

1 tablespoon honey

1 tablespoon vanilla extract

1 tablespoon trans-free margarine

1 banana, cut into 12 slices

12 raspberries

WHISK together ¼ cup of the milk, the egg yolks, sugar, cornstarch, honey, and vanilla in a large bowl.

HEAT the remaining 2 cups milk in a small saucepan over medium heat for 4 minutes, or just until it starts to simmer. Whisking constantly, slowly pour the hot milk into the yolk mixture until well combined. Pour the milk mixture back into the saucepan and bring to a boil, whisking constantly. Boil for 1 minute, or until thickened.

REMOVE from the heat and whisk in the margarine until melted. Immediately pour into 4 dessert dishes. Press a small piece of plastic wrap directly onto the surface of the puddings to prevent skins from forming. Refrigerate for at least 3 hours.

TOP each pudding with 3 banana slices and raspberries just before serving.

TOTAL TIME: 15 minutes + chilling time **MAKES 4 SERVINGS**

PER SERVING: 281 calories, 7 g protein, 53 g carbohydrates, 5 g total fat, 1 g saturated fat, 1 g fiber, 99 mg sodium

Tapioca Pudding

Extracted from the root of the cassava plant, tapioca is a starchy substance that's commonly used as a thickening agent. If stored in a cool, dark place, uncooked tapioca will keep indefinitely.

3 tablespoons quick-cooking tapioca

⅓ cup sugar

2 eggs

¼ teaspoon ground cardamom

¼ teaspoon ground cinnamon

4 cups fat-free milk

¼ cup dried cherries, blueberries, or raisins

1 teaspoon vanilla extract

MIX the tapioca, sugar, eggs, cardamom, and cinnamon in a medium saucepan until smooth. Stir in the milk. Bring to a boil over medium heat. Reduce the heat to low and simmer, stirring constantly, for 5 minutes.

REMOVE from the heat and stir in the cherries, blueberries, or raisins and vanilla. Pour into a serving bowl and press a piece of plastic wrap directly onto the surface to prevent a skin from forming. Refrigerate until cold.

TOTAL TIME: 15 minutes + chilling time **MAKES 8 SERVINGS**

PER SERVING: 122 calories, 6 g protein, 22 g carbohydrates, 1 g total fat, 0.5 g saturated fat, 1 g fiber, 70 mg sodium

Coconut Rice Pudding with Raspberries

This rice pudding recipe saves some calories by drawing its nutty flavor from coconut extract and bypassing the richness of coconut milk. It's easy to make in single servings, but you can multiply the recipe if it becomes a family favorite.

¾ cup water

¼ cup instant brown rice

2 tablespoons nonfat dry milk

1 teaspoon honey

⅛ teaspoon coconut extract

½ cup fresh or frozen and thawed raspberries

COMBINE the water and rice in a microwaveable mixing bowl or 8-cup glass measuring cup. Stir. Cover with plastic wrap, leaving a small vent for steam to escape. Microwave on high power for 5 minutes. Reduce the power to medium and microwave for 3 minutes longer.

REMOVE from the microwave oven and let stand for 5 minutes to allow the rice to soften. Carefully remove the plastic. Stir in the dry milk, honey, and coconut extract. Gently fold in the raspberries. Spoon the mixture into a cereal bowl to serve.

TOTAL TIME: 20 minutes **MAKES 1 SERVING**

PER SERVING: 170 calories, 6 g protein, 35 g carbohydrates, 1 g total fat, 0 g saturated fat, 5 g fiber, 59 mg sodium

Fresh and Dried Fruit Crisp

Dried apricots add texture and a bit of tangy contrast to the classic summer pairing of peaches and blueberries.

1½ pounds peaches, sliced

3 cups blueberries

1 cup dried apricots, sliced

1 cup firmly packed light brown sugar, divided

1 tablespoon cornstarch

1 teaspoon vanilla extract

¾ teaspoon ground ginger

½ cup quick-cooking oats

½ cup whole grain pastry flour

½ cup sliced almonds

3 tablespoons trans-free margarine

PREHEAT the oven to 375°F. Coat a 2-quart baking dish with cooking spray.

TOSS together the peaches, blueberries, apricots, ½ cup of the sugar, cornstarch, vanilla, and ginger in a large bowl. Pour into the baking dish.

COMBINE the oats, flour, almonds, margarine, and remaining ½ cup sugar in a separate large bowl. Rub the mixture together with your fingers until it resembles coarse crumbs and begins to form clumps when squeezed. Sprinkle over the peach mixture.

BAKE for 35 minutes, or until the filling is thick and bubbling and the top is lightly browned.

TOTAL TIME: 1 hour **MAKES 8 SERVINGS**

PER SERVING: 307 calories, 5 g protein, 61 g carbohydrates, 7 g total fat, 1 g saturated fat, 5 g fiber, 34 mg sodium

Gingered Autumn Fruit Crisp

Perfect for a casual dinner party, this dessert takes only a few minutes to assemble and can be slipped in the oven while the rest of your meal bakes.

- **3 tablespoons confectioners' sugar**
- **2 teaspoons cornstarch**
- **2 cups sliced Anjou or Bartlett pears (1 pound)**
- **2 cups sliced McIntosh apples (1 pound)**
- **2 cups sliced red or purple plums (1 pound)**
- **2 tablespoons finely chopped crystallized ginger**
- **2 teaspoons vanilla extract**
- **¾ cup old-fashioned oats**
- **2 tablespoons firmly packed brown sugar**
- **½ teaspoon apple pie spice**
- **2 tablespoons cold trans-free margarine spread**

PREHEAT the oven to 350°F. Coat an 8" × 8" baking dish with cooking spray.

COMBINE the confectioners' sugar and cornstarch in a large bowl. Stir until well blended. Add the pears, apples, plums, ginger, and vanilla. Toss to coat evenly. Transfer to the baking dish. Set aside.

WIPE the bowl dry with a paper towel. Add the oats, brown sugar, and apple pie spice. Toss with a fork to mix. With the fork, break the spread into small chunks. Add to the mixture. Use the fork to cut into smaller pieces that blend with the oats mixture. Scatter over the fruit mixture.

BAKE for 55 minutes, or until golden brown and bubbly. Let stand for 10 minutes before serving. Serve warm or at room temperature.

TOTAL TIME: 1 hour 30 minutes **MAKES 8 SERVINGS**

PER SERVING: 149 calories, 2 g protein, 31 g carbohydrates, 3 g total fat, 0.5 g saturated fat, 4 g fiber, 22 mg sodium

Enlightened Brownies

These brownies are exceptionally fluffy, thanks to the addition of extra egg whites, but the flavor is all chocolate.

½ cup cake flour

½ cup unsweetened cocoa powder

¼ teaspoon baking powder

¼ teaspoon salt

1 egg

2 egg whites

¾ cup sugar

½ cup vegetable oil

1½ teaspoons vanilla extract

2 tablespoons chopped pistachios or walnuts

PREHEAT the oven to 350°F. Coat an 8" × 8" baking pan with cooking spray.

SIFT together the flour, cocoa, baking powder, and salt in a medium bowl. Set aside.

WHISK the egg and egg whites in a large bowl until frothy. Whisk in the sugar, oil, and vanilla until smooth. Gradually fold in the flour mixture until just blended. Pour into the baking pan. Sprinkle with the nuts.

BAKE for 20 to 25 minutes, or until a wooden pick inserted in the center comes out with moist crumbs. Cool in the pan on a rack. Cut into 12 squares.

TOTAL TIME: 30 minutes **MAKES 12**

PER BROWNIE: 175 calories, 3 g protein, 20 g carbohydrates, 11 g total fat, 1.5 g saturated fat, 1 g fiber, 73 mg sodium

Chocolate Cream Pie

Fancy food trends abound, but nothing is more comforting than the tried-and-true dishes we all grew up with. What could be more satisfying and delicious than a slice of rich chocolate cream pie?

CRUST

- **10 whole low-fat graham crackers**
- **¼ cup walnuts**
- **3 tablespoons sugar**
- **2 tablespoons unsalted butter, melted**

FILLING

- **2¾ cups fat-free milk**
- **1 cup sugar**
- **1 egg**
- **¼ cup unsweetened cocoa powder**
- **¼ cup cornstarch**
- **¼ teaspoon salt**
- **1 teaspoon unsalted butter**

TO MAKE THE CRUST

PREHEAT the oven to 350°F. Coat a 9" pie plate with cooking spray.

PROCESS the graham crackers, walnuts, and sugar in a food processor until fine crumbs form. Add the butter and pulse just until blended. Press the mixture into the bottom and up the sides of the pie plate. Bake for 10 minutes, or until lightly browned. Cool on a wire rack for 10 minutes.

TO MAKE THE FILLING

MEANWHILE, whisk together the milk, sugar, egg, cocoa, cornstarch, and salt in a large saucepan until well combined. Whisking constantly, bring to a low boil over medium heat. Cook, whisking frequently, for 5 minutes, or until thickened. Remove from the heat and whisk in the butter until melted.

PRESS a piece of plastic wrap directly onto the surface of the filling to prevent a skin from forming and let cool for 20 minutes. Chill the filling in the refrigerator for 1 hour, or until completely cooled.

REMOVE the plastic wrap and spread the filling into the crust. Refrigerate for at least 2 hours before cutting into 8 slices.

TOTAL TIME: 35 minutes + cooling and chilling times **MAKES 8 SERVINGS**

PER SERVING: 251 calories, 5 g protein, 44 g carbohydrates, 7 g total fat, 3 g saturated fat, 1 g fiber, 160 mg sodium

Mini Turnovers with Raspberries

Wonton wrappers aren't just for adventures in Chinese cooking. Here, they provide a terrific means to encase a lightly sweetened cheese filling in this elegant alternative to dessert cookies.

1½ **cups raspberries**

2 **tablespoons honey, divided**

½ **cup part-skim ricotta cheese**

1 **teaspoon all-purpose flour**

¼ **teaspoon ground cardamom**

12 **wonton wrappers**

PREHEAT the oven to 350°F. Coat a baking sheet with cooking spray.

COMBINE the raspberries and 1 tablespoon of the honey in a medium bowl, tossing to coat. Set aside. Stir together the ricotta, flour, cardamom, and remaining 1 tablespoon honey in a separate small bowl.

PLACE the wrappers on a flat surface and place a scant tablespoon of the ricotta mixture in the center of each. Moisten the edges of each wrapper with water and fold 1 corner over to form a triangle. Press the sides together to seal. Place the turnovers on the baking sheet. Lightly coat the tops with cooking spray.

BAKE for 12 minutes, or until browned. Cool on a rack for at least 10 minutes. Place 3 turnovers each on 4 plates. Top with the raspberry mixture.

TOTAL TIME: 45 minutes **MAKES 4 SERVINGS**

PER SERVING: 174 calories, 7 g protein, 30 g carbohydrates, 4 g total fat, 2 g saturated fat, 4 g fiber, 171 mg sodium

Pistachio Baklava

Pistachios, which are rich in calcium, thiamin, phosphorus, iron, and vitamin A, shine in this traditional Middle Eastern dessert.

- **3 cups unsalted pistachios, coarsely chopped**
- **⅓ cup sugar**
- **2 teaspoons grated orange peel**
- **¼ teaspoon ground cloves**
- **⅛ teaspoon salt**
- **Butter-flavored cooking spray**
- **24 sheets (17" × 12" each) frozen phyllo dough, thawed and halved crosswise**
- **1 tablespoon water**
- **¾ cup honey**
- **¼ cup fresh orange juice**
- **1 tablespoon fresh lemon juice**
- **½ teaspoon ground cardamom**

PREHEAT the oven to 350°F. Combine the pistachios, sugar, orange peel, cloves, and salt in a medium bowl and set aside.

LIGHTLY coat a 13" × 9" baking dish with the cooking spray. Working with 1 phyllo sheet at a time, place the sheet lengthwise in the bottom of the dish, allowing 1 end to extend over the edge of the dish, and lightly coat with the cooking spray. Repeat the procedure with 5 phyllo sheets and the cooking spray, alternating which sides overlap from layer to layer, for a total of 6 layers.

SPRINKLE evenly with one-third of the pistachio mixture (1 cup). Repeat layering the next 6 phyllo sheets, each lightly coated with the cooking spray, followed by the pistachio mixture. Lightly coat the top 6 sheets with cooking spray and press gently into the dish. Sprinkle the surface with the water.

MAKE 6 even lengthwise cuts and 6 even crosswise cuts, using a sharp knife, to form 36 portions. Bake for 30 minutes, or until the phyllo is golden brown. Remove from the oven.

MEANWHILE, combine the honey, orange juice, lemon juice, and cardamom in a medium saucepan over low heat. Cook for 2 minutes, or until the honey dissolves completely.

DRIZZLE the honey mixture over the baklava. Place the pan on a rack and cool completely.

TOTAL TIME: 1 hour 10 minutes **MAKES 36 SERVINGS**

PER SERVING: 284 calories, 7 g protein, 39 g carbohydrates, 12 g total fat, 2 g saturated fat, 3 g fiber, 159 mg sodium

Fruit Pizza

This is essentially the same dough used in the Rustic Tomato Pizza on page 207. However, a little more sugar is used to enhance the sweetness.

1 tablespoon sugar

1 package active dry yeast

1 cup warm water (105°F to 115°F)

3½ cups all-purpose flour, divided

1 teaspoon salt

1 tablespoon olive oil

2 teaspoons yellow cornmeal

8 ounces reduced-fat cream cheese

4 cups berries (any kind)

½ cup slivered almonds

¼ cup honey

2 tablespoons grated orange peel

DISSOLVE the sugar and yeast in the water in a large bowl. Let stand for 5 minutes.

COMBINE 3¼ cups of the flour and the salt in a food processor or bowl of an electric mixer fitted with a dough hook. Add the yeast mixture and oil through the feed tube. Process just until the dough comes together (the dough will be slightly sticky).

TURN the dough out onto a lightly floured surface. Knead until smooth and elastic (4 to 7 minutes). Add the remaining flour, 1 tablespoon at a time. Place the dough in a large bowl coated with cooking spray, and turn the dough to coat it. Cover and let rise in a warm place (85°F), free from drafts, for 1 hour.

PUNCH the dough down. Cover and let stand for 5 minutes. Line a baking sheet with parchment paper and sprinkle with cornmeal. Roll the dough into a 12" circle on a floured surface. Divide the dough into 4 pieces and place on the baking sheet. Crimp the edges of the dough. Let rise for 10 minutes.

PREHEAT the oven to 475°F.

SPREAD the cream cheese over the dough and scatter the berries on top. Bake 10 minutes. Sprinkle with the almonds and bake 5 minutes longer, or until the crust is browned. Drizzle with the honey and sprinkle with the orange peel. Cut in half and serve.

TOTAL TIME: 1 hour 45 minutes **MAKES 8 SERVINGS**

PER SERVING: 385 calories, 11 g protein, 65 g carbohydrates, 10 g total fat, 3 g saturated fat, 4 g fiber, 428 mg sodium

Cinnamon-Pecan Diamonds

Pecan butter cookies are always a decadent, melt-in-your-mouth delight. In this recipe, toasting the pecans brings out the flavor so you can use fewer (and save a few calories). They're as easy to make as a bar cookie, but much prettier!

1 **cup pecan pieces**

1½ **cups all-purpose flour**

½ **cup whole wheat flour**

1 **teaspoon ground cinnamon**

¼ **teaspoon salt**

½ **cup granulated sugar**

½ **cup butter**

¼ **cup 50/50 butter-blend spread, such as Smart Balance**

1 **teaspoon vanilla extract**

2 **tablespoons confectioners' sugar**

PREHEAT the oven to 350°F. Line a 9" × 9" baking pan with foil. Place the pecans on a baking sheet and toast in the oven for 10 minutes, or until fragrant. Cool.

WHISK the flours, cinnamon, and salt in a large bowl. In a mini food processor, chop the pecans with ⅓ cup of the flour mixture. Whisk back into the remaining flour mixture.

BEAT the granulated sugar, butter, spread, and vanilla in a medium bowl with an electric mixer on medium speed until combined. Add the flour mixture in thirds, beating on medium speed until combined.

PAT the dough evenly into the foil-lined baking pan. Lift the foil straight out of the pan and transfer the dough to the baking sheet. Score the dough crosswise into 8 strips. Score the dough on a diagonal into 10 strips (the outside strips will be corners that don't make full cookies). Bake for 25 minutes, or until the edges are golden brown.

CUT the cookies along the original score lines. Cool. Sift the confectioners' sugar over the cookies before serving.

TOTAL TIME: 50 minutes **MAKES 36**

PER COOKIE: 95 calories, 1 g protein, 9 g carbohydrates, 6 g total fat, 2 g saturated fat, 1 g fiber, 17 mg sodium

Oatmeal-Cranberry Chocolate Chip Cookies

The combination of oil and honey gives these cookies a moist and chewy texture. Mini chocolate chips spread well throughout the dough, so each cookie has bursts of chocolate.

1½ cups old-fashioned oats
½ cup all-purpose flour
½ cup whole wheat flour
½ teaspoon baking soda
½ teaspoon salt
½ teaspoon ground nutmeg
½ cup firmly packed brown sugar
¼ cup vegetable or canola oil
2 tablespoons honey
1 egg
1 teaspoon vanilla extract
¼ cup dried cranberries
¼ cup mini chocolate chips

PREHEAT the oven to 350°F. Coat a large baking sheet with cooking spray.

COMBINE the oats, flours, baking soda, salt, and nutmeg in a large bowl. Combine the sugar, oil, honey, egg, and vanilla in a medium bowl. Add to the oat mixture and stir until well blended. (The dough will be firm and sticky.) Fold in the cranberries and chocolate chips.

DROP the dough by scant teaspoonfuls onto the baking sheet. Press down slightly with damp fingers. Bake the cookies for 15 minutes, or until lightly browned.

TOTAL TIME: 30 minutes **MAKES 24**

PER COOKIE: 97 calories, 2 g protein, 15 g carbohydrates, 3 g total fat, 0.5 g saturated fat, 1 g fiber, 79 mg sodium

Granola Bars

Toasting the almonds and oats first intensifies their flavors and adds crunch. Almonds are a nutritional powerhouse, packed with calcium, fiber, folate, magnesium, potassium, riboflavin, and vitamin E.

1½ cups slivered almonds, divided

1½ cups rolled oats

1 tablespoon whole wheat pastry flour

⅔ cup chopped dried unsweetened cherries

2 eggs

1 cup firmly packed light brown sugar

1 tablespoon canola oil

1 teaspoon ground cinnamon

1 teaspoon vanilla extract

¼ teaspoon salt

PREHEAT the oven to 325°F. Line a 9" × 9" baking pan with foil, allowing about a 1" overhang on the sides. Coat with cooking spray.

PLACE the almonds and the oats on a large rimmed baking sheet. Bake for 10 minutes, or until toasted, stirring once.

TRANSFER the oat mixture to a food processor fitted with a metal blade. Add the flour. Process until coarsely chopped. Transfer to a medium bowl and combine with the cherries.

WHISK together the eggs, sugar, oil, cinnamon, vanilla, and salt in a large bowl. Add the oat mixture and stir until well blended. Spread in the foil-lined baking pan.

BAKE for 30 minutes, or until golden brown. Remove from the pan, using the foil as a handle, and cool completely on a rack. Cut into 12 portions with a serrated knife.

TOTAL TIME: 1 hour **MAKES 12**

PER BAR: 237 calories, 6 g protein, 34 g carbohydrates, 9 g total fat, 1 g saturated fat, 5 g fiber, 65 mg sodium

Walnut Shortbread

If you're not a big walnut fan, other nuts would work well in this shortbread, too. Try it with pecans, cashews, or almonds instead of the walnuts.

⅔ **cup walnut halves**

¾ **cup all-purpose flour**

½ **cup whole wheat flour**

½ **cup confectioners' sugar**

¼ **teaspoon salt**

¼ **cup walnut oil**

¼ **cup extra-light olive oil**

1½ **teaspoons grated lemon peel**

1 **teaspoon vanilla extract**

PREHEAT the oven to 325°F.

TOAST the nuts on a baking sheet in the oven for 10 minutes, or until fragrant.

COMBINE the all-purpose flour and walnuts in a food processor and process until the nuts are finely ground.

TRANSFER the flour-walnut mixture to a large bowl. Stir in the whole wheat flour, sugar, and salt. Add the oils, lemon peel, and vanilla and stir until well combined.

PRESS the dough into the bottom of a 9" tart pan with a removable bottom. With the tines of a fork, prick the dough. With a sharp knife, score the dough into 16 wedges, cutting almost, but not quite through, to the bottom.

BAKE for 30 minutes, or until crisp and lightly golden. Check after 20 minutes; if the shortbread is overbrowning, decrease the oven temperature to 300°F.

REMOVE from the oven and, while still warm, cut the wedges through to the bottom. Cool in the pan on a rack.

TOTAL TIME: 50 minutes **MAKES 16 SERVINGS**

PER SERVING: 137 calories, 2 g protein, 12 g carbohydrates, 10 g total fat, 1 g saturated fat, 1 g fiber, 37 mg sodium

Spiced Cranberry-Walnut Biscotti

Biscotti were created for dunking! Whether your choice is a steaming cup of tea, coffee, or hot chocolate, these crispy cookies are sure to satisfy.

¾ cup all-purpose flour

½ cup whole grain pastry flour

¾ teaspoon baking powder

1 teaspoon apple pie spice

3 tablespoons trans-free margarine, softened

3 tablespoons honey

½ teaspoon orange extract

1 egg

3 tablespoons fat-free milk

3 tablespoons chopped walnuts

3 tablespoons chopped dried cranberries

COMBINE the flours, baking powder, and spice on a sheet of waxed paper.

STIR with a fork to mix. Set aside.

COMBINE the margarine, honey, and orange extract in a mixing bowl. Beat with a wooden spoon until smooth and light. Add the egg, beating until smooth. Add the milk and beat until smooth. Gradually add the flour mixture, beating just until combined. Stir in the walnuts and cranberries. Cover with plastic wrap. Refrigerate for at least 3 hours, or until firm.

PREHEAT the oven to 325°F. Coat 2 baking sheets with cooking spray. Turn the dough out onto a lightly floured work surface and divide in half. Roll each piece of the dough into a 1"-diameter log. Place the logs, separated, on the baking sheet.

BAKE for 30 minutes, or until the logs are set. Remove to a rack to cool for 10 minutes. Reduce the oven temperature to 300°F.

CUT each log with a serrated knife into ½"-wide diagonal slices. Place the slices, cut sides down, on the baking sheets.

BAKE for 18 minutes, or until toasted on top. Turn the cookies and bake for about 10 minutes longer, or until toasted on top. Remove to racks to cool.

TOTAL TIME: 4 hours 25 minutes **MAKES 10 SERVINGS**

PER SERVING: 127 calories, 3 g protein, 19 g carbohydrates, 5 g total fat, 1 g saturated fat, 1 g fiber, 88 mg sodium

Rosemary Scones

The delicate herbal notes of this scone make it the perfect accompaniment for a brunch spread or an afternoon tea.

½ cup fat-free plain yogurt

1 egg

3 tablespoons butter, melted

1 teaspoon grated orange peel

4 tablespoons firmly packed brown sugar, divided

1¾ cups all-purpose flour

2 teaspoons baking powder

¼ teaspoon baking soda

1 tablespoon finely chopped fresh rosemary

PREHEAT the oven to 375°F.

WHISK together the yogurt, egg, butter, orange peel, and 3 tablespoons of the sugar in a medium bowl just until blended.

STIR together the flour, baking powder, baking soda, and rosemary in a large bowl. Make a well in the center of the flour mixture and add the yogurt mixture. Stir together just until combined. Do not overmix.

SPRINKLE a sheet of plastic wrap lightly with flour. Scrape the dough onto the plastic wrap and spread into a 7" circle. Sprinkle the top of the dough lightly with flour and pat until smooth. Invert the round onto a baking sheet and cut into 8 wedges, using a sharp, flour-dipped knife. Spoon the remaining 1 tablespoon sugar into a sieve and sprinkle evenly over the wedges.

BAKE for 15 to 17 minutes, or until golden. Cool on the baking sheet on a rack for 10 minutes.

TOTAL TIME: 35 minutes **MAKES 8**

PER SCONE: 167 calories, 4 g protein, 26 g carbohydrates, 5 g total fat, 3 g saturated fat, 1 g fiber, 190 mg sodium

Apricot-Ginger Buttermilk Scones

Dried apricots lend a tangy sweetness and a nice kick of fiber to these breakfast treats.

½ cup buttermilk

1 egg

3 tablespoons butter, melted

1 teaspoon grated fresh ginger

1 teaspoon grated lemon peel

4 tablespoons firmly packed brown sugar, divided

1¾ cups whole grain pastry flour

¼ cup chopped dried apricots (about 7 small whole apricots)

2 tablespoons chopped crystallized ginger

2 teaspoons baking powder

¼ teaspoon baking soda

Honey (optional)

PREHEAT the oven to 375°F.

WHISK together the buttermilk, egg, butter, fresh ginger, lemon peel, and 3 tablespoons of the sugar in a medium bowl just until blended.

STIR together the flour, apricots, crystallized ginger, baking powder, and baking soda in a large bowl. Make a well in the center of the flour mixture and add the buttermilk mixture. Stir together just until combined. Do not overmix.

SPRINKLE a sheet of plastic wrap lightly with flour. Scrape the dough onto the plastic wrap and spread into a 7" circle. Sprinkle the top of the dough lightly with flour and pat until smooth. Invert the round onto a baking sheet and score the top into 8 wedges, using a sharp, flour-dipped knife. Spoon the remaining 1 tablespoon sugar into a sieve and sprinkle evenly over the top.

BAKE for 15 to 17 minutes, or until golden. Cool on the baking sheet on a rack for 10 minutes. Cut into 8 wedges and serve with the honey, if desired.

TOTAL TIME: 35 minutes **MAKES 8**

PER SCONE: 170 calories, 4 g protein, 28 g carbohydrates, 5 g total fat, 3 g saturated fat, 2 g fiber, 198 mg sodium

Sweet Potato Spice Muffins

For optimal flavor, try baking your sweet potatoes to use in recipes like this. Simply rub the skins with a few drops of olive oil, cut a slit in the side, and roast in the oven at 375°F for 1 hour, or until soft. One medium-size sweet potato will provide about a cup of mashed potato.

2 cups whole wheat flour or whole grain pastry flour

½ cup sugar

1 tablespoon baking powder

½ teaspoon baking soda

½ teaspoon salt

½ teaspoon ground cinnamon

¼ teaspoon ground nutmeg

1½ cups cooked, mashed sweet potatoes

½ cup water

½ cup raisins

PREHEAT the oven to 375°F.

COMBINE the flour, sugar, baking powder, baking soda, salt, cinnamon, and nutmeg in a large bowl. Add the sweet potatoes, water, and raisins and stir until just mixed.

COAT a 12-cup muffin pan with cooking spray. Fill the cups to the top with batter.

BAKE for 25 to 30 minutes, or until the top of a muffin bounces back when pressed lightly. Let stand for 1 to 2 minutes before removing from the pan. When cool, store in an airtight container in the refrigerator.

TOTAL TIME: 40 minutes **MAKES 12**

PER MUFFIN: 142 calories, 3 g protein, 34 g carbohydrates, 1 g total fat, 0 g saturated fat, 4 g fiber, 275 mg sodium

The Best Bran Muffins

These muffins are guaranteed not to be dry because they are infused with a delicious orange syrup after baking.

2 cups shredded all-bran cereal

¾ cup hot water

¼ cup canola oil

1 orange

¾ cup buttermilk

2 tablespoons light molasses

2 tablespoons honey

1 egg

1¼ cups whole grain pastry flour

⅓ cup old-fashioned oats

2 teaspoons baking soda

½ teaspoon salt

1 cup dried cranberries

¼ cup chopped toasted walnuts (optional)

¼ cup sugar

PREHEAT the oven to 400°F. Coat a 12-cup muffin pan with cooking spray.

COMBINE the cereal, water, and oil in a medium bowl. Stir until the cereal is softened.

GRATE 1 tablespoon of the peel from the orange into another medium bowl. Cut the orange in half and squeeze the juice into a separate bowl. (You should have ½ cup juice.) Add ¼ cup of the juice to the bowl with the orange peel, reserving the remaining juice. Add the buttermilk, molasses, honey, and egg and stir until well blended. Stir into the cereal mixture.

COMBINE the flour, oats, baking soda, and salt in a large bowl. Add the cereal mixture and stir just until blended. Stir in the cranberries and walnuts, if using.

DIVIDE the batter among the muffin cups. Bake for 15 minutes, or until a wooden pick inserted in the center of a muffin comes out clean. Remove from the oven and set on a rack.

MEANWHILE, combine the sugar and reserved ¼ cup orange juice in a small saucepan. Bring to a boil over medium heat and stir until the sugar dissolves. Using a wooden pick, poke a few small holes in the muffin tops. Brush with the orange syrup.

REMOVE from the pan and cool completely on the rack.

TOTAL TIME: 35 minutes **MAKES 12**

PER MUFFIN: 199 calories, 4 g protein, 36 g carbohydrates, 6 g total fat, 0.5 g saturated fat, 5 g fiber, 356 mg sodium

Find the Fat

Almost every dairy product comes in a regular version plus at least one lower-fat version. (Our recipes specify exactly which to use.) The wording on the label can help guide you. Reduced-fat means at least 25 percent less fat than the traditional version. Low-fat foods have no more than 3 grams of fat per serving, and fat-free have less than ½ gram. A "light" food has one-third fewer calories and at least 50 percent less fat.

REGULAR VERSION	LOWER-FAT ALTERNATIVE	FAT-FREE ALTERNATIVE
CHEDDAR CHEESE SHREDS	**REDUCED-FAT CHEDDAR CHEESE SHREDS**	**FAT-FREE CHEDDAR CHEESE SHREDS**
1 tablespoon	1 tablespoon	1 tablespoon
30 calories	20 calories	10 calories
SOUR CREAM	**LIGHT SOUR CREAM**	**FAT-FREE (0%) PLAIN GREEK YOGURT**
1 tablespoon	1 tablespoon	1 tablespoon
25 calories	20 calories	10 calories
WHOLE MILK	**LOW-FAT 1% MILK**	**FAT-FREE MILK**
1 cup	1 cup	1 cup
150 calories	100 calories	80 calories
PLAIN YOGURT	**LOW-FAT PLAIN YOGURT**	**FAT-FREE PLAIN YOGURT**
6 ounces	6 ounces	6 ounces
140 calories	110 calories	100 calories
BUTTER	**WHIPPED BUTTER**	**FAT-FREE BUTTER GRANULES**
1 teaspoon	1 teaspoon	1 teaspoon
30 calories	20 calories	5 calories
HALF-AND-HALF	**LOW-FAT NONDAIRY CREAMER**	**FAT-FREE HALF-AND-HALF**
1 tablespoon	1 tablespoon	1 tablespoon
20 calories	10 calories	10 calories

CHAPTER

15

Menus for Special Times

TO HELP YOU REACH your goals and enjoy meals that are celebration-worthy, we've put together some sample menus to inspire you and provide a healthy starting point for planning. Whatever the occasion, these recipes are guaranteed to give you what you need, with minimal prep work and fuss.

Each menu includes a one-serving nutritional analysis and sometimes recommended nonrecipe sides that you can easily factor into your daily eating plan. The portion size for all recipes listed is one serving. And because *Prevention* magazine recommends that you limit saturated fat intake to 10 percent of total calories—about 17 grams per day for most women—and sodium intake to less than 2,300 milligrams, we've noted with an asterisk (*) which menus are slightly high in these nutrients so you can remember to be mindful of your choices for the rest of the day.

Big Family Breakfast

Pancakes with Blueberry Syrup, page 65

Turkey Sausage, page 51

Coffee or tea

PER SERVING: 475 calories, 36 g protein,
67 g carbohydrates, 8 g total fat,
1 g saturated fat, 5 g fiber, 663 mg sodium

Weekend Brunch

Spinach-Tomato Frittata, page 197

Rosemary Scones, page 333

4 ounces fresh orange juice

PER SERVING: 535 calories, 27 g protein,
56 g carbohydrates, 23 g total fat,
8 g saturated fat*, 6 g fiber, 625 mg sodium

Tailgate Party

Meatless Muffulettas, page 93

½ cup carrot and celery sticks

Oatmeal-Cranberry Chocolate Chip Cookies, page 327

PER SERVING: 389 calories, 14 g protein, 47 g carbohydrates, 17 g total fat, 6 g saturated fat, 5 g fiber, 956 mg sodium*

A Summer Picnic

Quick Turkey-Veggie Wrap, page 82

Watermelon Salad, page 151

Sugar-free iced tea or lemonade

PER SERVING: 585 calories, 47 g protein, 60 g carbohydrates, 22 g total fat, 6 g saturated fat, 8 g fiber, 655 mg sodium

Springtime Celebration

Mediterranean Couscous, page 183

Pistachio Baklava, page 323

PER SERVING: 547 calories, 15 g protein,
77 g carbohydrates, 22 g total fat,
3 g saturated fat, 7 g fiber, 433 mg sodium

Family Movie Night!

Classic Veggie Pizzas, page 209

Enlightened Brownies, page 319

PER SERVING: 451 calories, 14 g protein,
59 g carbohydrates, 20 g total fat,
4 g saturated fat, 5 g fiber, 687 mg sodium

Let's Eat In!

Better-Than-Takeout Pad Thai, page 221

Hot green tea

PER SERVING: 381 calories, 11 g protein,
68 g carbohydrates, 8 g total fat,
1 g saturated fat, 3 g fiber, 910 mg sodium*

Cinco de Mayo!

Meatless Tacos, page 229

Grilled Peaches with Macaroons and
Caramel Sauce, page 311

PER SERVING: 619 calories, 19 g protein,
108 g carbohydrates, 14 g total fat,
5 g saturated fat, 18 g fiber, 857 mg sodium*

Cozy Winter Meal with Friends

Russian Beet and Bean Soup, page 125

1 slice pumpernickel bread

Black tea

PER SERVING: 205 calories, 9 g protein, 40 g carbohydrates, 2 g total fat, 0.5 g saturated fat, 8 g fiber, 790 mg sodium

Father's Day Surprise

Greek-Seasoned Filet of Beef with Cucumber Tzatziki, page 277

Walnut Shortbread, page 330

PER SERVING: 461 calories, 38 g protein, 37 g carbohydrates, 19 g total fat, 4 g saturated fat, 7 g fiber, 374 mg sodium

An Easy Sunday Supper

Caribbean Getaway

Rosemary Roasted Chicken and Vegetables, page 265

Gingered Autumn Fruit Crisp, page 318

PER SERVING: 388 calories, 21 g protein, 64 g carbohydrates, 6 g total fat, 1 g saturated fat, 13 g fiber, 279 mg sodium

Jamaican-Style Scallops with Black Bean Salsa, page 243

Fruit Kebabs with Raspberry-Mango Dip, page 305

PER SERVING: 629 calories, 30 g protein, 77 g carbohydrates, 26 g total fat, 3 g saturated fat, 12 g fiber, 362 mg sodium

Valentine's Day

Roast Cod with Pomegranate-Walnut Sauce,
page 238

Chocolate Cream Pie, page 321

PER SERVING: 727 calories, 44 g protein,
86 g carbohydrates, 23 g total fat,
4 g saturated fat, 6 g fiber, 278 mg sodium

Backyard Pool Party

Tropical Veggie Burgers, page 97

Homemade Fruity Yogurt Pops, page 309

PER SERVING: 445 calories, 23 g protein,
63 g carbohydrates, 13 g total fat,
4 g saturated fat, 9 g fiber, 647 mg sodium

Photo Credits

© Tom Rafalovich: page viii

© Kana Okada: page 4

© John Ragel: pages 6, 8, 12

© Mitch Mandel/Rodale: pages 15, 16, 72, 80, 89, 102, 124, 136, 154, 166, 170, 175, 190, 196, 232, 236, 244, 250, 252, 256, 260, 264, 268, 274, 276, 278, 298, 286, 294, 304, 308, 312, 316, 320, 340 (right), 344, 345, 346

© Perry Hagiopan: pages 17 (right), 26, 36

© Hugh Kretschmer: pages 18, 22

© Claire Benoist: page 28

© Noah Fecks: page 32

© Shannon Hammer: page 37

© Thomas MacDonald/Rodale: pages 39, 57, 68, 70, 96, 108, 150, 159, 162, 240, 248, 272, 282, 290, 302, 328, 341 (right)

© Quentin Bacon: pages 40, 44, 48, 52, 61, 64, 76, 84, 92, 100, 106, 112, 116, 120, 128, 133, 138, 142, 148, 172, 178, 182, 186, 192, 194, 200, 204, 208, 212, 216, 220, 224, 228, 300, 324, 332, 336, 340 (left), 341 (left), 342, 343

The photos on page 17 (left), page 27 (left), and page 27 (right) were supplied courtesy of the test panelists.

Index

Underscored page references indicate sidebars and tables.
Boldface references indicate photographs.

///